THE RIGHT SPACE

A Wheelchair Accessibility Guide for Single-Family Homes

A. M. Ayala

DEBOLD - MARQUEZ BOOKS

First printing: March 2005

Copyright © 2005 by Debold - Marquez Books, LLC

City, county, and state laws may be more stringent
than the ADA Accessibility Guidelines, the International
Building Code, industry standards, or the guidelines
contained in this book.

Published by Debold - Marquez Books
1900 W. Chandler Boulevard, Suite 15-282
Chandler, Arizona 85224
Fax: 480 821 2929

ISBN 0-9764432-4-4

Printed in the United States of America

For additional copies of the *The Right Space* visit our
website at www.trspace.com

CONTENTS

INTRODUCTION

The Right Space illustrates what is essential for wheelchair accessibility: the ability to enter your own home, use any fixture in any order, turn around and leave. Being able to accomplish that means a person lives in an accessible home.

In the United States, people in wheelchairs can move freely through public spaces because of the Americans with Disabilities Act (ADA). Single-family homes, typically, do not have the same freedom of movement. They do have a growing number of men and women advocating design and construction practices that facilitate home accessibility regardless of age or ability.

It is important to note that new construction or renovation must conform to local requirements. City, county, and state laws may be more stringent than the ADA Accessibility Guidelines, the International Building Code, industry standards, or the guidelines contained in this book.

This guide's several hundred three-dimensional pictures illustrate basic floor spaces and fixtures within a home's first floor using notes, suggestions, and relevant ADA specifications. The illustrations begin with the clear floor space a wheelchair occupies at all times. Succeeding pictures follow a path from a sidewalk, to an entrance door, and into a bathroom and a kitchen. They illustrate turning spaces, doors, landings, ramps, and high and low reach. Also examined are the relationships between adjacent fixtures and the turning spaces allowing access from one fixture to another.

This guide's goal is to create an aware consumer, one able to ask building or real estate professionals the right questions to ensure that every path, every space, and every fixture in his or her home has received special consideration.

GLOSSARY AND NOTES

ACCESSIBLE
The ability to approach, reach, enter, or use.

ACCESSIBLE ROUTE
An interior or exterior circulation path.

APPROACH DIRECTION
a. A forward approach assumes reach or use may be in front of a person.
b. A parallel approach assumes reach or use may be beside a person.

CLEAR FLOOR SPACE
a. The zone of comfort surrounding a wheelchair everywhere it goes is a wheelchair's clear floor space.
b. The width and depth of a floor surface making a particular fixture accessible is that fixture's clear floor space.

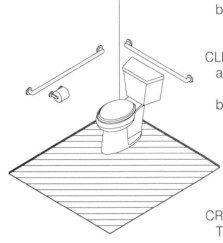

CROSS SLOPE
The slope ninety degrees to the direction of travel.

KNEE AND TOE SPACE
A contact-free zone.

FINISHED FLOOR
The accessible floor surface a wheelchair travels on.

FIXTURE
The basic fixtures found in single-family homes.

knee space
toe space

RAMP
An accessible route with a running slope steeper than 1 : 20 is a ramp.

ROUGH-IN DIMENSION
The distance between two structural walls before a wall covering is applied.

RUNNING SLOPE
The slope in the same direction of travel.

WATER CLOSET
The designation given to a toilet.

GLOSSARY AND NOTES

WIDTH, HEIGHT, AND DEPTH
    a. Width is the horizontal distance 90 degrees to the direction of approach or use.
    b. Height is the vertical distance above the finished floor, if any.
    c. Depth is the horizontal distance in the same direction of approach or use.

Throughout this guide, the width-height-depth order is used when describing dimensions. The width and depth of a wheelchair clear floor space is an example.

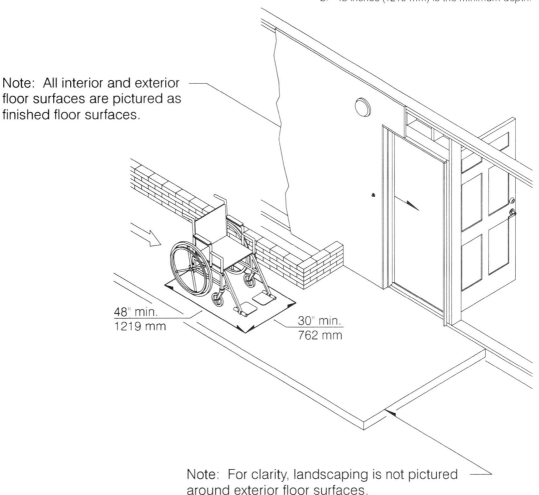

WHEELCHAIR CLEAR FLOOR SPACE
    a. 30 inches (762 mm) is the minimum width.
    b. 48 inches (1219 mm) is the minimum depth.

Note: All interior and exterior floor surfaces are pictured as finished floor surfaces.

48" min.
1219 mm

30" min.
762 mm

Note: For clarity, landscaping is not pictured around exterior floor surfaces.

NOTES

PRIMARY FLOOR SURFACES

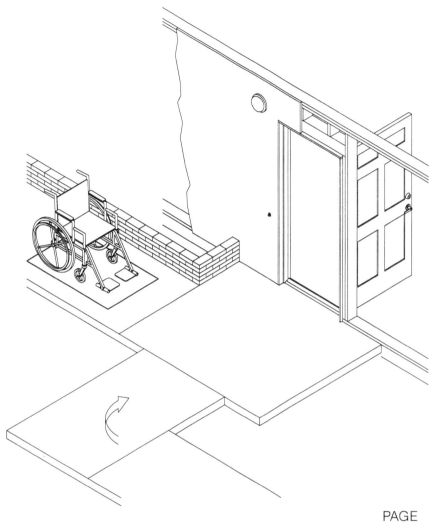

PRIMARY FLOOR SURFACES   11

WIDTH, DEPTH, AND SLOPE

Accessible routes have firm, stable, slip resistant floor surfaces.
Accessible routes also have guidelines for width, depth, and slope.

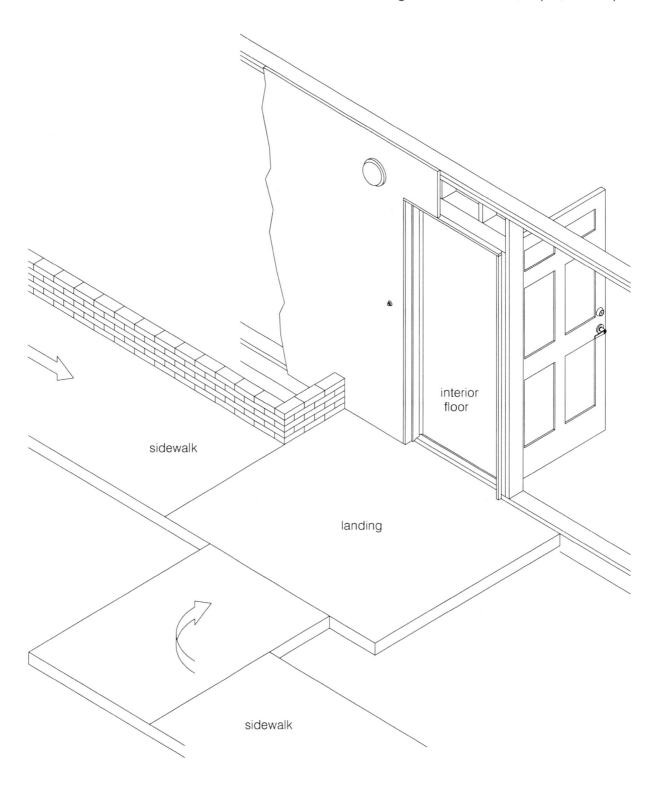

interior
floor

sidewalk

landing

sidewalk

For wheelchair access the constant rule is, every interior floor surface and every exterior floor surface must be an accessible floor surface.

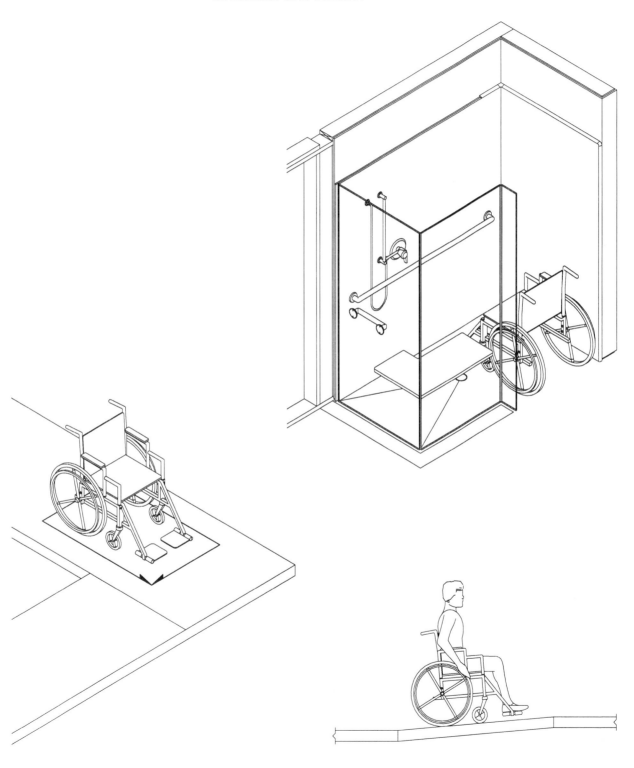

WHEELCHAIR CLEAR FLOOR SPACE
a. 30 inches (762 mm) is the minimum width.
b. 48 inches (1219 mm) is the minimum depth.

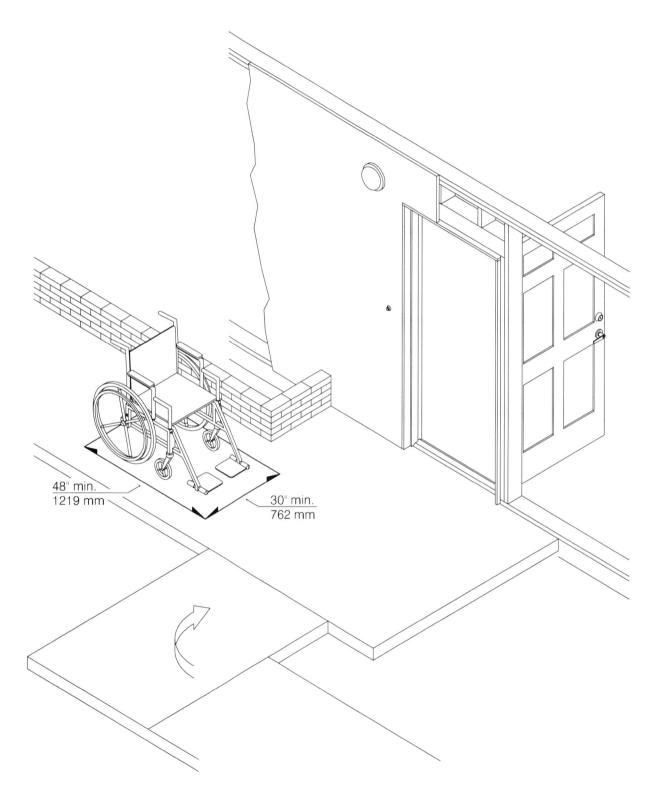

48" min.
1219 mm

30" min.
762 mm

A wheelchair clear floor space is a zone of comfort surrounding a wheelchair everywhere it goes.

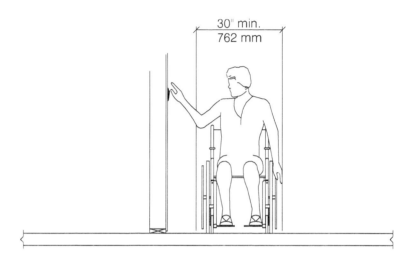

30" min.
762 mm

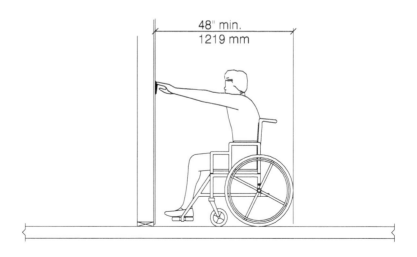

48" min.
1219 mm

MINIMUM WIDTH
  36 inches (914 mm) is the minimum width of an accessible route
  more than 24 inches (610 mm) in depth. Sidewalks, landings,
  and ramps are examples.

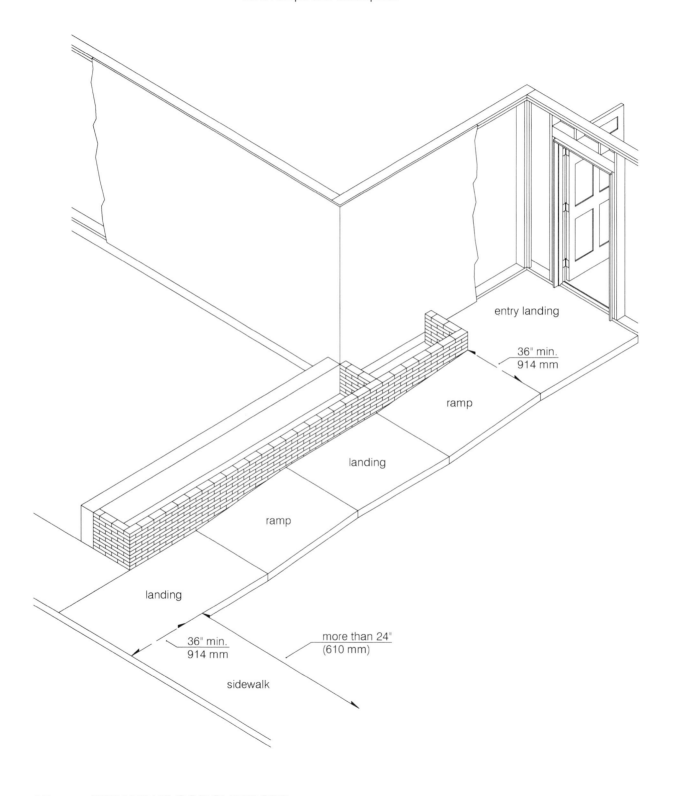

MINIMUM WIDTH (continued)
   32 inches (813 mm) is the minimum width of an accessible route
   24 inches (610 mm) or less in depth.

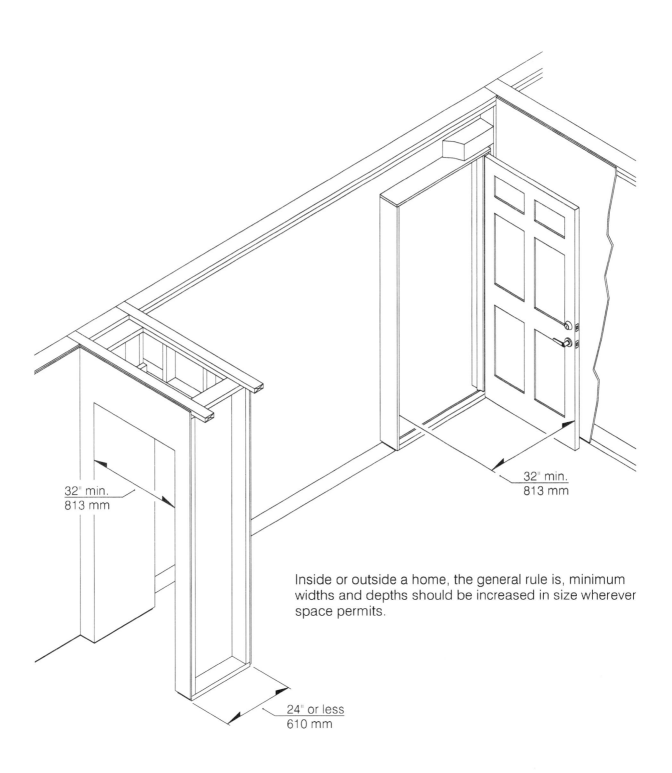

32" min.
813 mm

32" min.
813 mm

Inside or outside a home, the general rule is, minimum
widths and depths should be increased in size wherever
space permits.

24" or less
610 mm

RUNNING SLOPE
An accessible route with a running slope of 1 : 20 or less
is not a ramp.

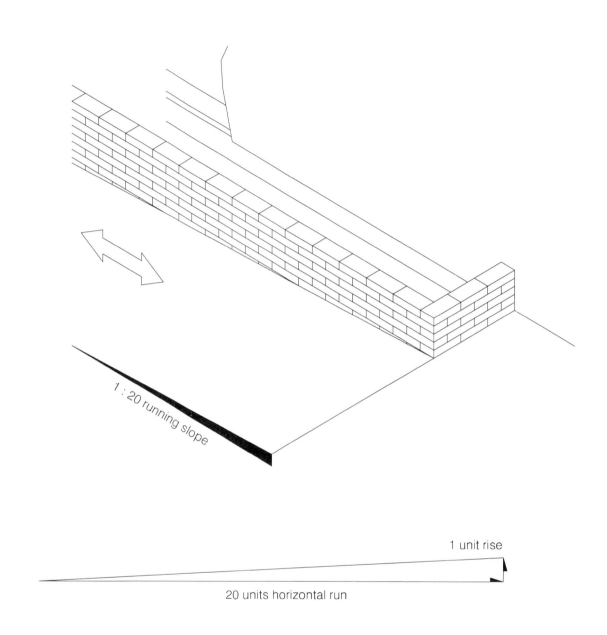

1 unit rise

20 units horizontal run

1 : 20 rise and corresponding run

1" (25.4 mm) rise = 20" (508 mm) horizontal run	3-5/8" (92.1 mm) rise = 72" (1829 mm) horizontal run
1-7/8" (47.6 mm) rise = 36" (914 mm) horizontal run	4-7/8" (123.8 mm) rise = 96" (2438 mm) horizontal run
2-3/8" (60.3 mm) rise = 48" (1219 mm) horizontal run	12" (305 mm) rise = 20' (6.10 m) horizontal run

A floor surface that rises or falls in the direction of travel has a running slope. When an accessible route is relatively flat, when it is not a ramp, that accessible route has a minimum width and an unlimited depth.

Note: An accessible route steeper than 1 : 20 is a ramp. A ramp's width, depth, and slope guidelines are on page 63.

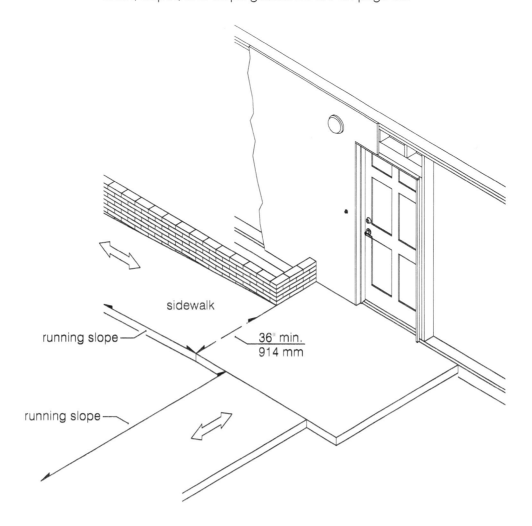

Four components make up a running slope.
1. A running slope has a two unit designation such as 1 : 20.
2. The first number is the vertical change in height, always 1 unit.
3. The second number is the horizontal distance in like units.
4. As the second number becomes larger, the slope becomes flatter.

Example: 1 : 40 is a flatter slope than 1 : 20.

CROSS SLOPE
1 : 48 is the maximum cross slope of an accessible route.

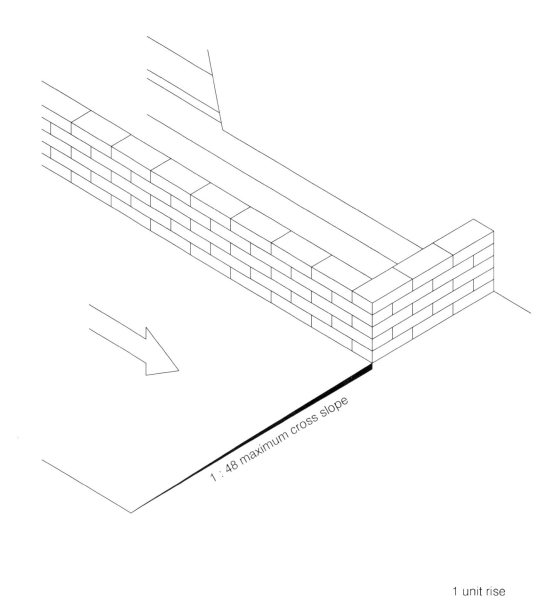

1 : 48 maximum cross slope

1 unit rise

48 units horizontal run

1 : 48 rise and corresponding run

3/4" (19.1 mm) rise = 36" (914 mm) horizontal run	1-1/8" (28.6 mm) rise = 54" (1372 mm) horizontal run
7/8" (22.2 mm) rise = 42" (1067 mm) horizontal run	1-1/4" (31.8 mm) rise = 60" (1524 mm) horizontal run
1" (25.4 mm) rise = 48" (1219 mm) horizontal run	1-1/2" (38.1 mm) rise = 72" (1829 mm) horizontal run

A cross slope, the slope ninety degrees to the direction of travel, plays an important role in shedding water away from exterior walls and entrance doors.

An example of excessive cross slope is a pathway that requires a constant course correction. A pathway demanding that much exertion is not an accessible route.

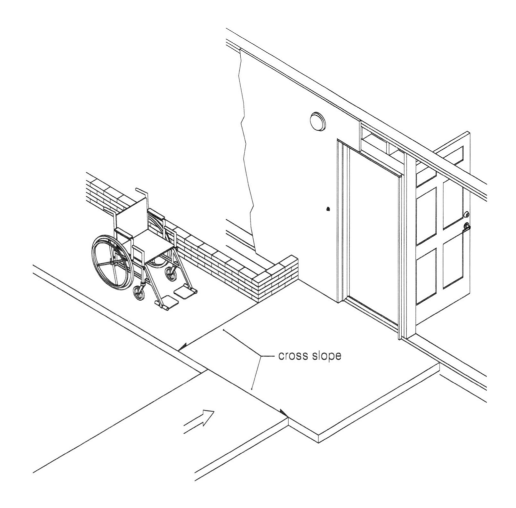

cross slope

Four components make up a cross slope.
1. A cross slope has a two unit designation such as 1 : 48.
2. The first number is the vertical change in height, always 1 unit.
3. The second number is the horizontal distance in like units.
4. As the second number becomes larger, the slope becomes flatter.

Example: 1 : 80 is a flatter slope than 1 : 50.

VERTICAL CHANGE IN LEVEL
  1/4 inch (6.35 mm) is the maximum vertical change in level
  from one floor surface to another.

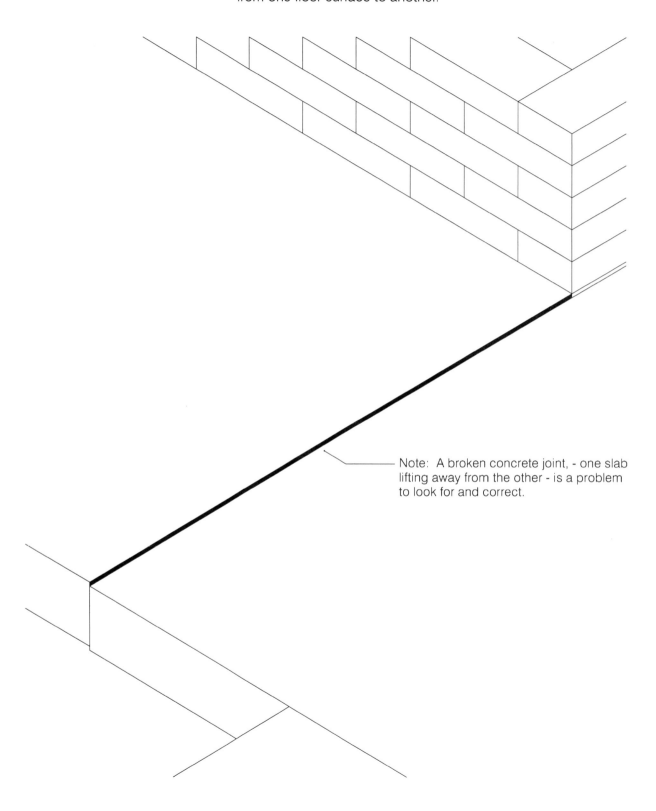

Note: A broken concrete joint, - one slab
lifting away from the other - is a problem
to look for and correct.

A smooth transition from floor surface to floor surface is the ideal. The reality is, changes in level are commonplace.

A quarter-inch tall threshold at a doorway is a typical application. A quarter-inch difference in height from the bathroom floor to the shower floor is another.

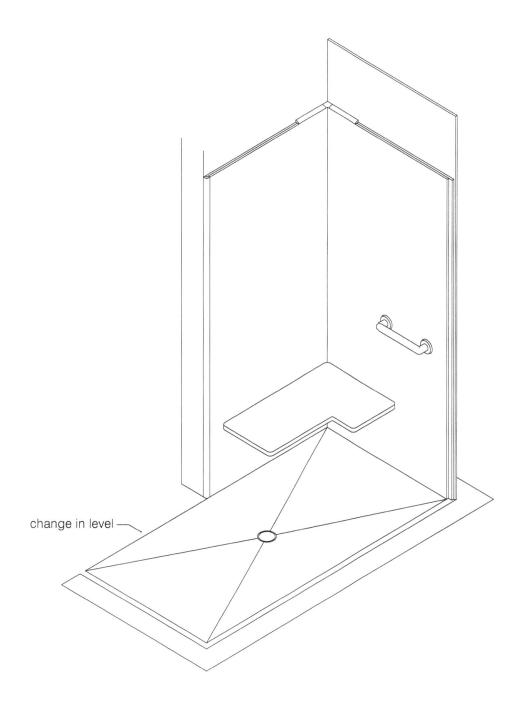

change in level

BEVELED CHANGE IN LEVEL
    a. 1/2 inch (12.7 mm) is the maximum height.
    b. 1 : 2 is the maximum running slope.

Note: A locality may allow an exception at a sliding door and allow a 3/4 inch (19.05 mm) maximum height provided the sliding door has a threshold with a 1 : 2 bevel on both sides.

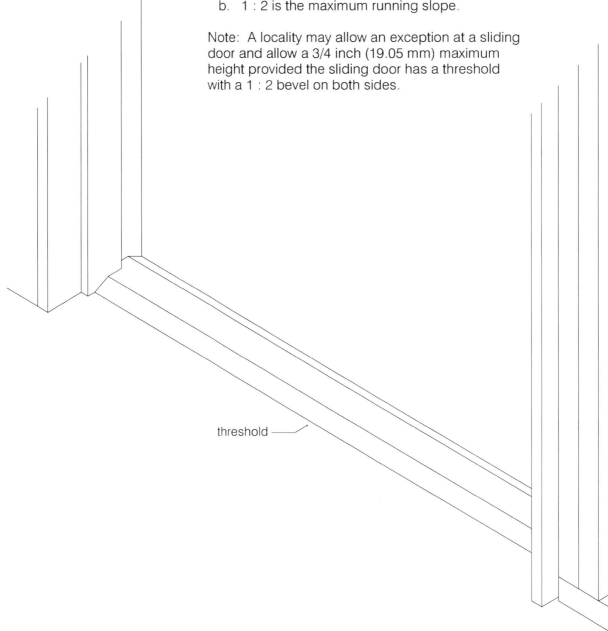

threshold

2 units horizontal

1 unit rise

1/2" maximum
(12.7 mm)

A threshold at an entrance door is a familiar change in level that creates a beveled transition from floor surface to floor surface.

To ensure a smooth transition, the finished floor on either side of the threshold has to be established.

Other views of a floor surface to floor surface transition are on page 27.

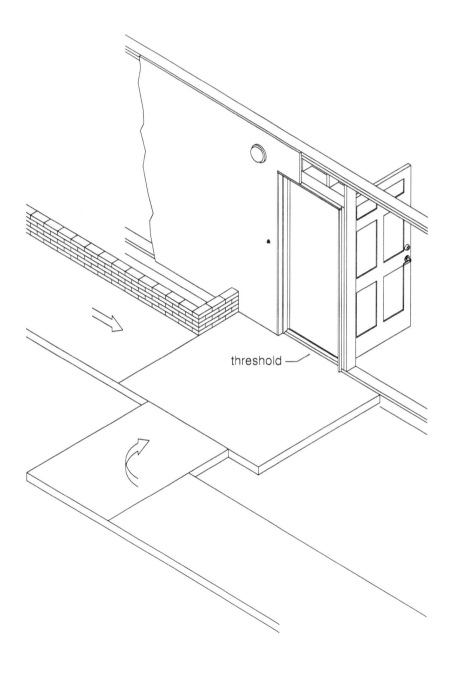

threshold —

FLOOR TILE
Floor tile must be slip resistant.

CARPET
- 1/2 inch (12.7 mm) is the maximum pile height.
- All exposed edges require trim.

Note: The combination of pad and carpet, or carpet by itself, must be firm and stable. Also, a lower pile height will improve maneuverability.

DECK OR GRATE SPACING
1/2 inch (12.7 mm) is the maximum width between deck boards or grating.

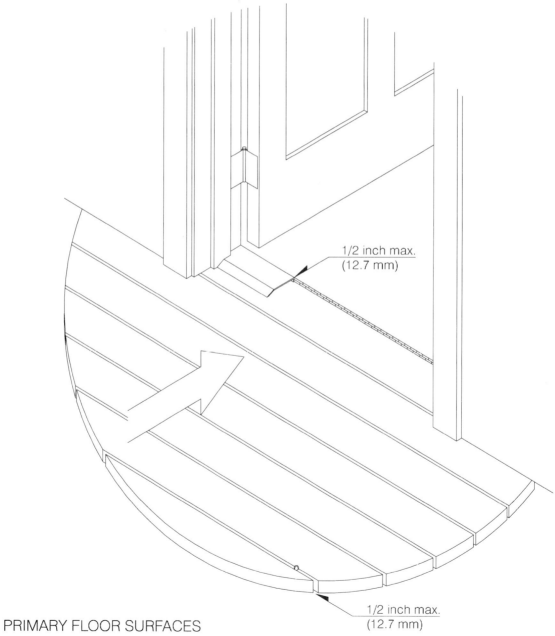

1/2 inch max.
(12.7 mm)

1/2 inch max.
(12.7 mm)

Floor Tile

Floor tile must be slip resistant. The grout joints between tiles must also adhere to the guidelines for a beveled or a vertical change in level.

When backer board is included in a subfloor's design, the transition from floor surface to floor surface can be reduced to zero by choosing the right combination of tile and board.

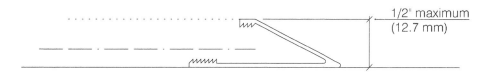

Carpet Trim

Carpet trim must create a change in level that a wheelchair can roll across without excessive effort.

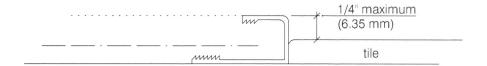

The change in level from one floor surface to another determines whether a transition has a 1 : 2 bevel or a vertical change in level.

Deck and Grate Spacing

Deck boards or elongated spaces between grating should run perpendicular to the predominant direction of travel.

NOTES

TURNING

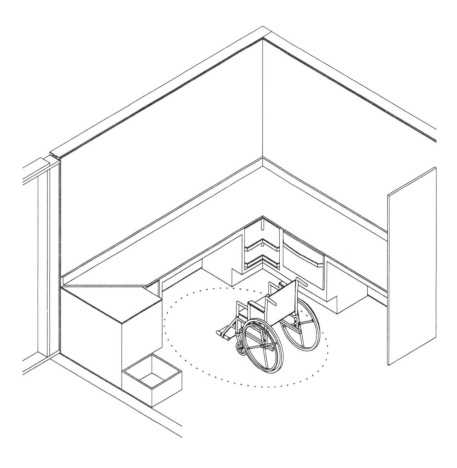

TURNING SPACES

Interior and exterior turning spaces are firm, stable, slip resistant, and 1 : 48 is the maximum cross slope and running slope.

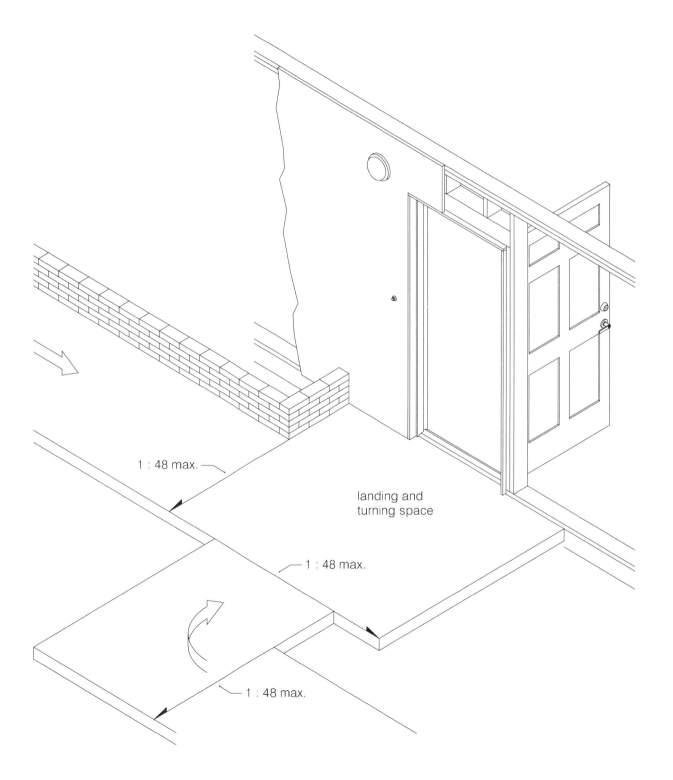

1 : 48 max.

landing and
turning space

1 : 48 max.

1 : 48 max.

Although turning spaces have minimum widths and depths, those minimums are guidelines. The general rule is, minimum widths and depths should be increased in size wherever space permits.

The Elliptical turning space below is an example.

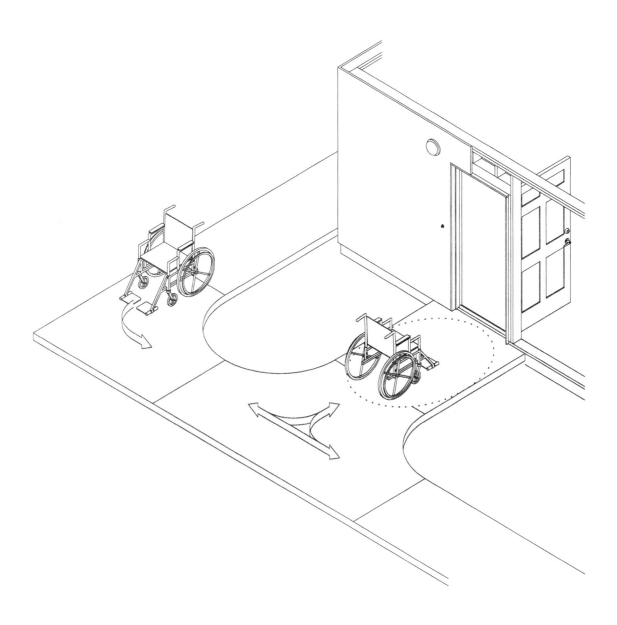

90 DEGREE TURN

A t-shape, with a 36 inch (914 mm) minimum width both in and out of the turn, is an example of a 90 degree turn.

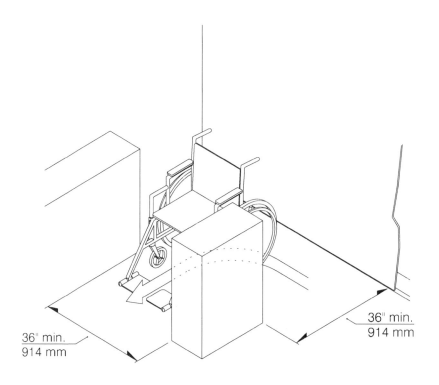

36" min.
914 mm

36" min.
914 mm

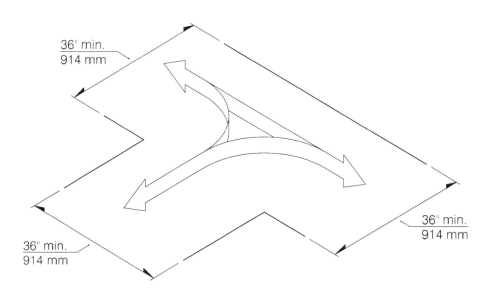

36" min.
914 mm

36" min.
914 mm

36" min.
914 mm

90 DEGREE TURN
Through a Doorway

An accessible doorway has a floor space on either side
called a landing. There is no all-encompassing guideline
for a doorway's landing size because:

- A landing's width and depth have several determining factors.
  Approach direction, hardware location, and door swing are
  only three of the considerations.

The entrance landing and interior landing sections on pages
49 and 87 detail landing sizes.

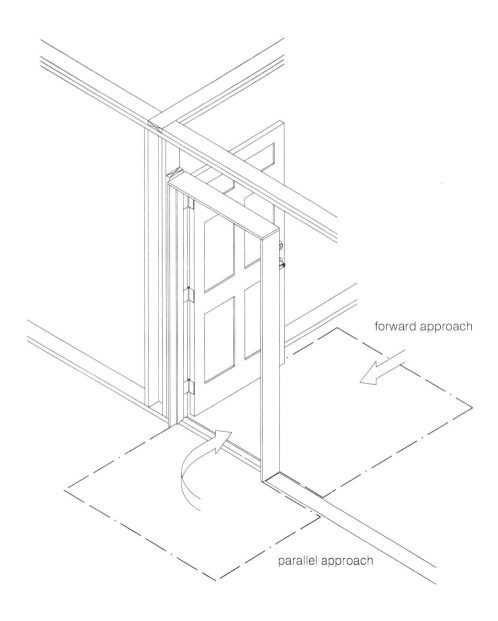

forward approach

parallel approach

ASSOCIATED 90 DEGREE TURNS
Turn One
When the distance between two 90 degree turns is less than
48 inches (1219 mm), if routes A and C are 42 inches (1067 mm)
minimum in width, 48 inches is the minimum width of route B.

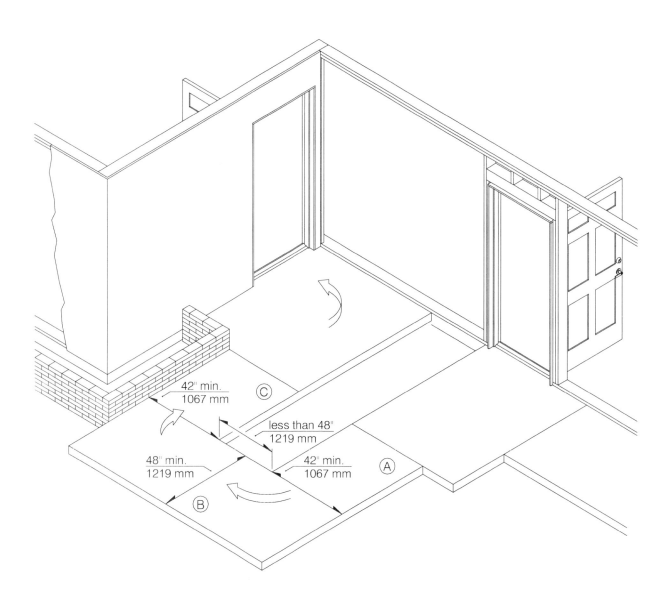

42" min.
1067 mm

C

less than 48"
1219 mm

48" min.
1219 mm

42" min.
1067 mm

A

B

ASSOCIATED 90 DEGREE TURNS
Turn Two
When the distance between two 90 degree turns is less than 48 inches (1219 mm), if routes A and C are 36 inches (914 mm) minimum in width, 60 inches (1524 mm) is the minimum width of route B.

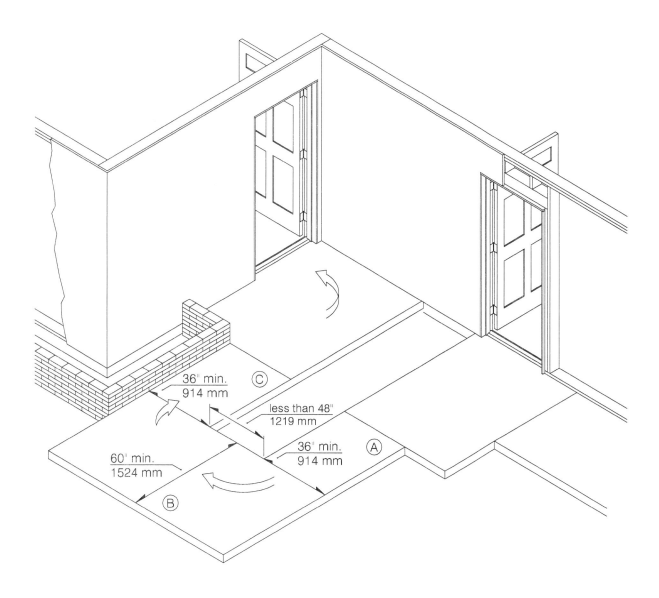

36" min.
914 mm

©

less than 48"
1219 mm

36" min.
914 mm

Ⓐ

60" min.
1524 mm

Ⓑ

CIRCULAR TURNING SPACE
60 inches (1524 mm) is the minimum diameter of a Circular turning space.

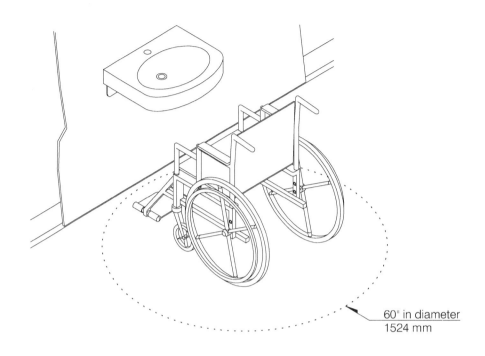

60" in diameter
1524 mm

Knee space and toe space beneath an ADA compliant lavatory is illustrated below. Knee and toe space guidelines are on page 132.

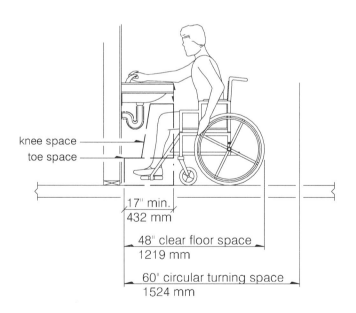

knee space
toe space

17" min.
432 mm

48" clear floor space
1219 mm

60" circular turning space
1524 mm

T - SHAPED TURNING SPACE
Within a 60 by 60 inch (1524 x 1524 mm) Square
a. Two arms and a base are 36 inches (914 mm) wide minimum.
b. Both arms are clear of obstructions 12 inches (305 mm) minimum in each direction.
c. The base is clear of obstructions 24 inches (610 mm) minimum.
d. The end of one arm or the base can include knee and toe space clearance.

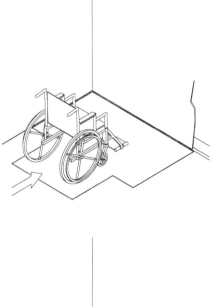

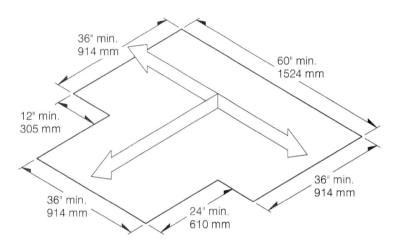

36" min.
914 mm

60" min.
1524 mm

12" min.
305 mm

36" min.
914 mm

36" min.
914 mm

24" min.
610 mm

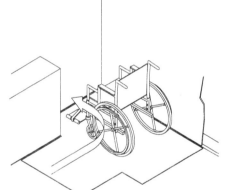

Note: This series of 90 degree turns within the confines of the T - shape requires backing and filling while wheels and toes are repeatedly, if not in contact with perimeter walls, very close to them.

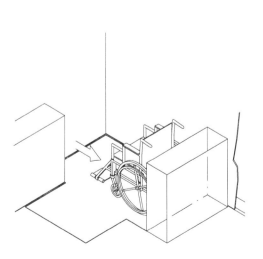

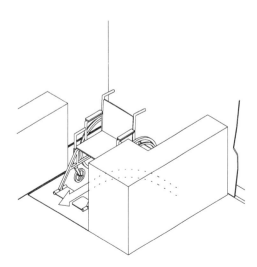

ELLIPTICAL TURNING SPACE

A 60 by 78 inches (1524 x 1981 mm) Elliptical turning space
is an easier space to turn around in than the Circular turning
space.

An Elliptical turning space can also take advantage of knee
and toe space below an ADA compliant fixture requiring knee
clearance.

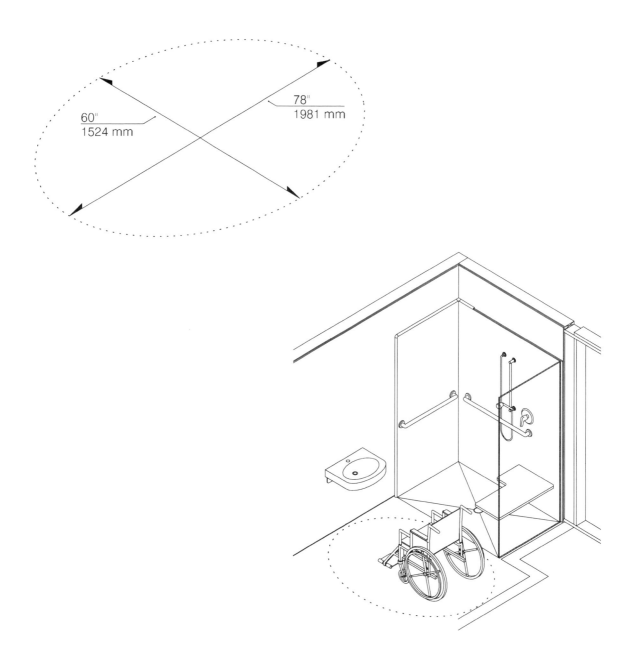

TURNING NOTES

- The Elliptical turning space provides the most room for a 180 degree turn.

- The Circular turning space is smaller, requiring thought and care while turning.

- The T - shaped turning space, is the most restricting turning space.

The circles or ellipses in the remainder of this guide are 60 inch (1524 mm) in diameter circles or 60 x 78 inch (1524 x 1981 mm) ellipses.

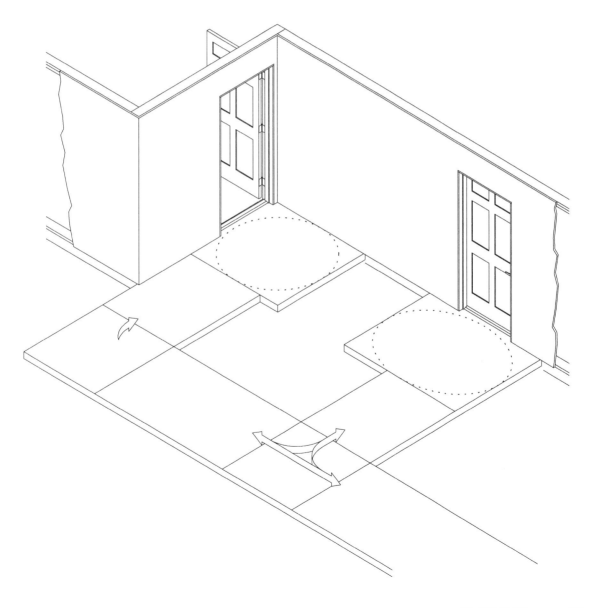

NOTES

DOORS AND PASSAGEWAYS

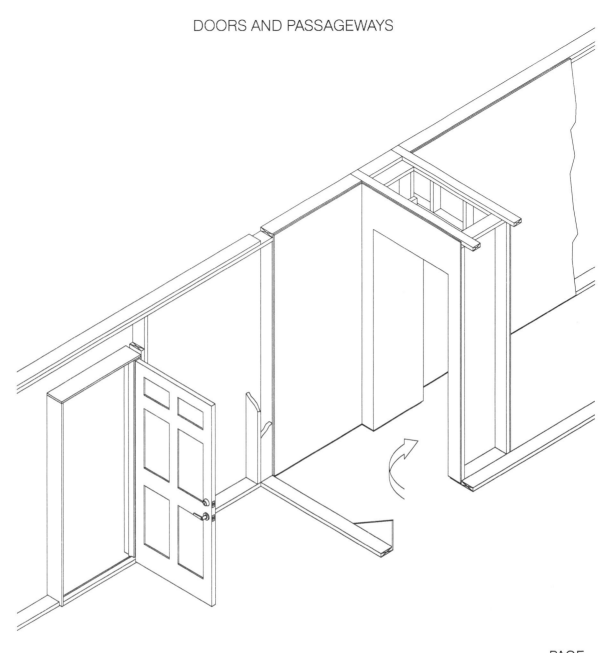

HINGED DOOR

32 inches (813 mm) is the minimum width between door and doorstop when the door is open 90 degrees.

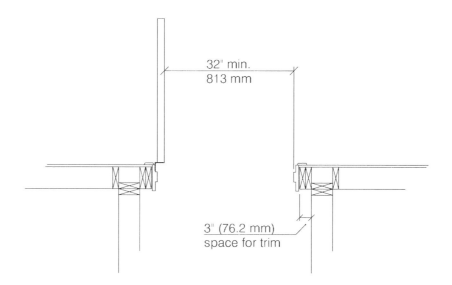

32" min.
813 mm

3" (76.2 mm)
space for trim

In the United States, the "standard" sized hinged door that meets the 32 inch minimum width guideline is the 3068 door.

- 30 is shorthand for 3 feet and 0 inches in width (914 mm).
- 68 is shorthand for 6 feet and 8 inches in height (2032 mm).

The width between the doorstop and the edge of a 3068 door open at 90 degrees is approximately 33-1/2 inches (851 mm).

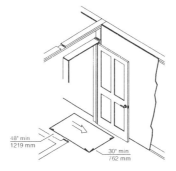

WHEELCHAIR CLEAR FLOOR SPACE
a. 30 inches (762 mm) is the minimum width.
b. 48 inches (1219 mm) is the minimum depth.

48" min
1219 mm

30" min.
762 mm

The next size smaller "standard" door is the 2868 door. The width between the doorstop and the edge of this door when it is open 90 degrees is approximately 29-1/2 inches (749 mm).

- 28 is shorthand for 2 feet and 8 inches in width (813 mm).
- 68 is shorthand for 6 feet and 8 inches in height (2032 mm).

HINGED DOOR
  Typical Guidelines
    a. Width
          32 inches (813 mm) minimum between door
          and doorstop when the door is open 90 degrees.
    b. Solid kick surface
          10 inches (254 mm) minimum
          above the finished floor.
    c. Hardware height
          34 inches (864 mm) minimum and
          48 inches (1219 mm) maximum
          above the finished floor.
    d. Latch type
          Easy to grasp. Lever shaped handles at a hinged
          door are typical.

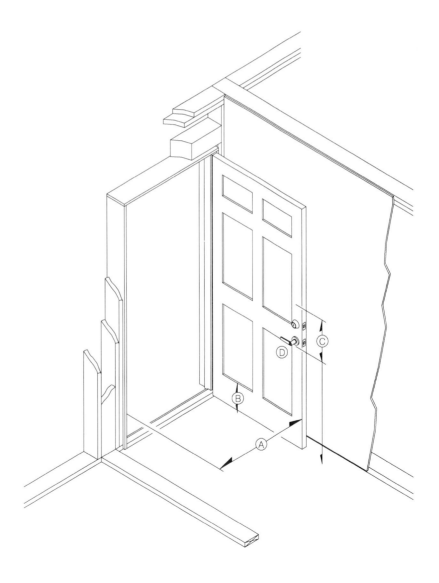

DOUBLE DOORS

32 inches (813 mm) is the minimum width between the inactive doorstop and the active door open at 90 degrees.

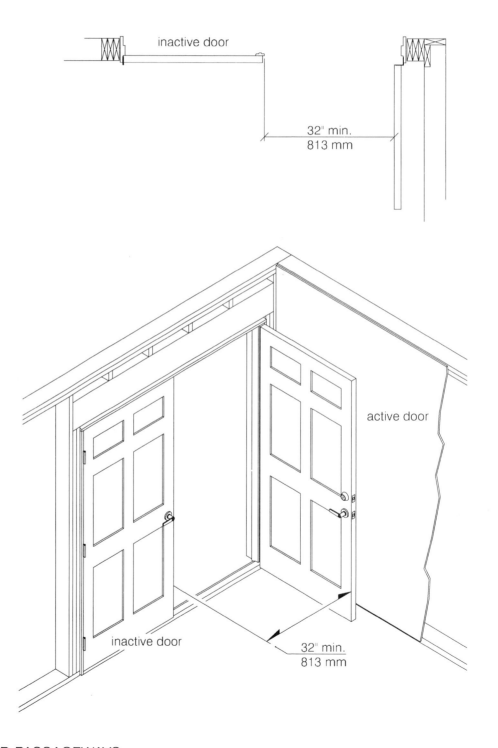

inactive door

32" min.
813 mm

active door

inactive door

32" min.
813 mm

POCKET DOOR AND FOLDING DOOR
32 inches (813 mm) is the minimum width between the
doorstop and the edge of an open sliding or folding door.

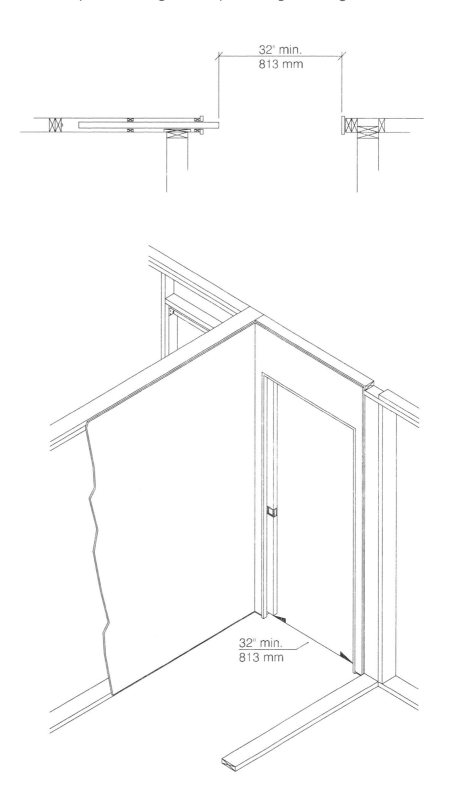

32" min.
813 mm

32" min.
813 mm

PASSAGEWAY WIDTH
a. 36 inches (914 mm) is the minimum width of a passageway more than 24 inches (610 mm) in depth.
b. 32 inches (813 mm) is the minimum width of a passageway 24 inches (610 mm) or less in depth. Consecutive 32 inch wide segments must have a 36 x 48 inch (914 x 1219 mm) unobstructed floor space separating them.

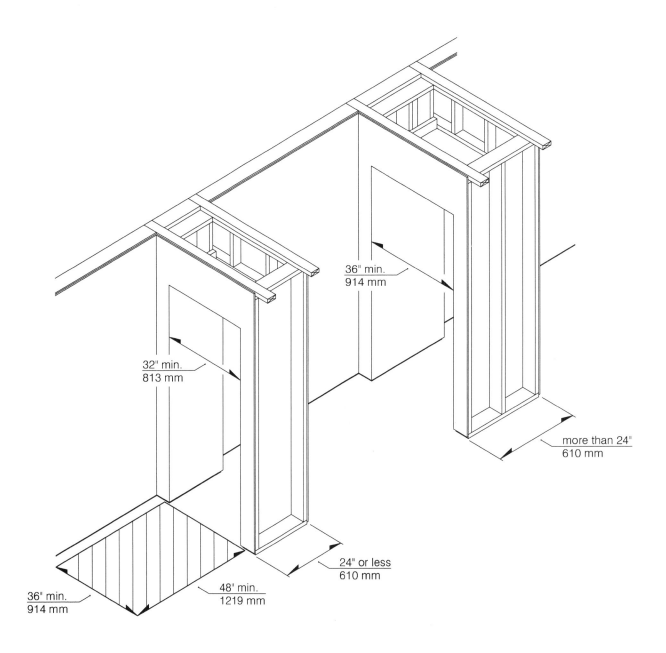

36" min.
914 mm

32" min.
813 mm

more than 24"
610 mm

24" or less
610 mm

48" min.
1219 mm

36" min.
914 mm

DOORWAY AND PASSAGEWAY NOTES

- A doorway or a passageway has a landing
  on either side.

- A doorway or a passageway has a forward approach
  or a parallel approach.

- A landing's width and depth have several determining factors.
  Approach direction, hardware location, and door swing are
  only three of the considerations.

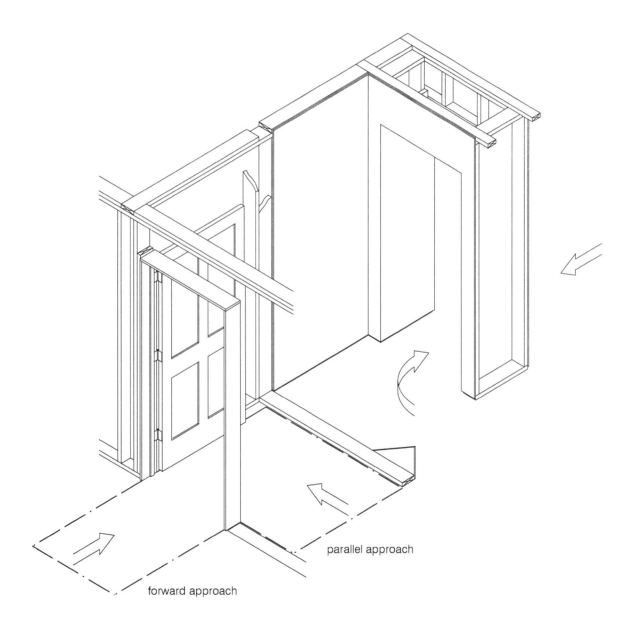

parallel approach

forward approach

NOTES

ENTRANCE LANDINGS

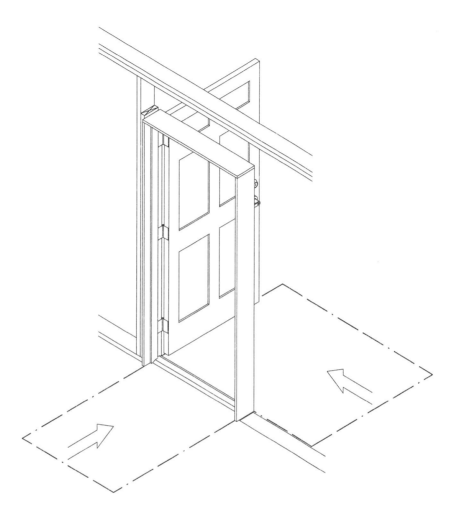

	PAGE

DESIGN CONSIDERATIONS

An accessible doorway has a floor space on either side
called a landing. An interior landing on the other side of
the entrance door is an example. Landings are firm, stable,
slip resistant, and 1 : 48 is the maximum cross slope and
running slope.

A landing on each side of a doorway or a passageway is
a constant. It is a landing's size that is variable.

HINGED DOOR

32 inches (813 mm) is the minimum width between
door and doorstop when the door is open 90 degrees.

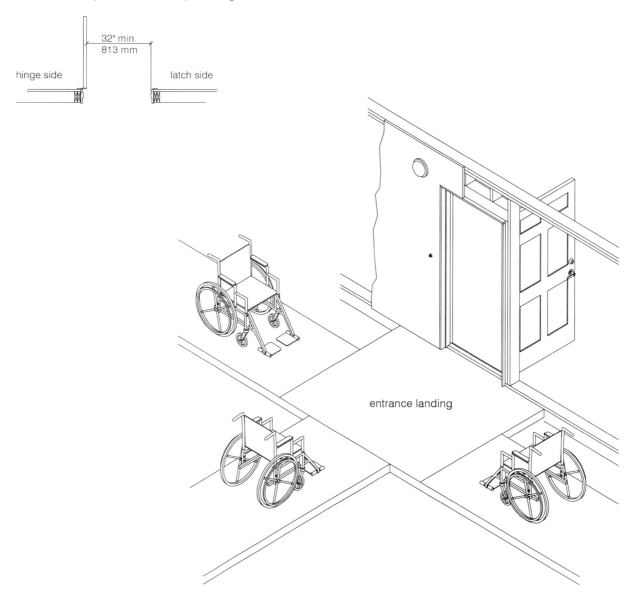

32" min.
813 mm

hinge side   latch side

entrance landing

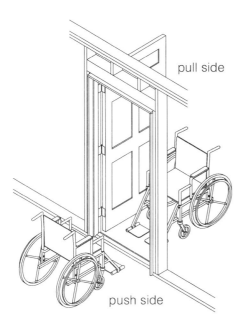

pull side

push side

Given the full width of an accessible doorway, landing considerations are:

Approach and Hardware Location
  Does a doorway have a forward approach?
  Does a doorway have a latch approach?
  Does a doorway have a hinge approach?

Door Swing
  Does a door push open?
  Does a door pull open?

Clearance Parallel to Doorway
  Does a doorway have clearance beyond the latch side or beyond the hinge side?

Closer
  Does a door have a closer?

Ramp
  Is a ramp attached to the landing? Examples are on pages 52, 54, 55, and 56.

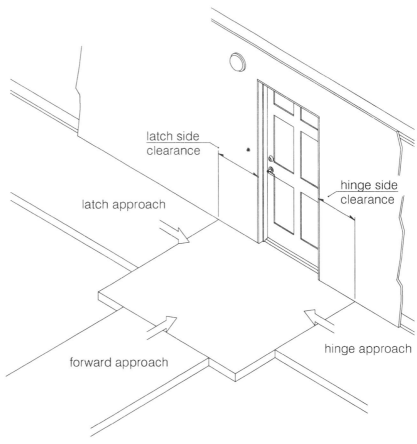

latch side clearance

hinge side clearance

latch approach

forward approach

hinge approach

FRONT APPROACH - PUSH SIDE LANDING
   a. 12 inches (305 mm) is the minimum clearance
       beyond the latch side if a closer and latch are provided.
   b. 48 inches (1219 mm) is the minimum depth.
   c. 60 inches (1524 mm) is the minimum depth
       when a ramp is attached.

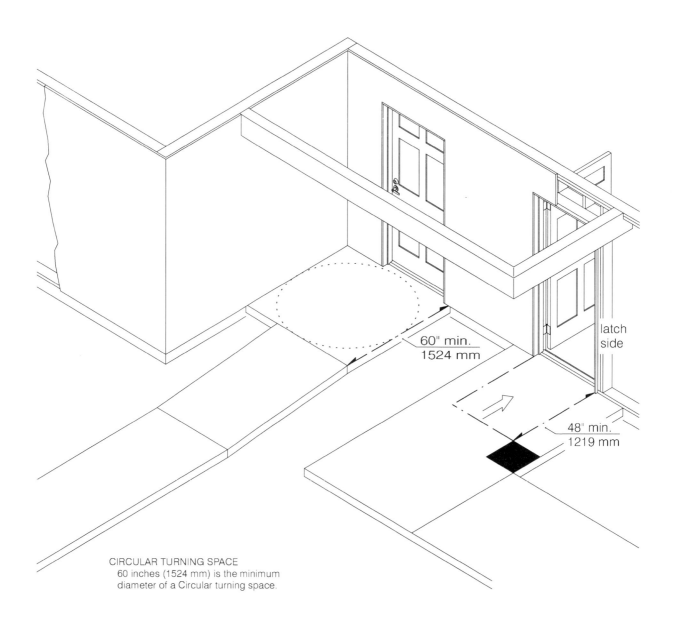

60" min.
1524 mm

latch
side

48" min.
1219 mm

CIRCULAR TURNING SPACE
  60 inches (1524 mm) is the minimum
  diameter of a Circular turning space.

Note: A landing with a minimum depth assumes the possibility
of an obstruction. Columns and pop-out details are examples
and must be taken into consideration when planning an entrance
landing.

FRONT APPROACH - PULL SIDE LANDING
   a.   18 inches (457 mm) is the minimum clearance
        beyond the latch side.
   b.   60 inches (1524 mm) is the minimum depth.

Security is a consideration. An exterior door swinging out
should have hinges with nonremovable (n.r.p.) pins.

A hinge's nonremovable pin cannot be pushed out when a
door is closed. To remove the pins, a retaining screw must
be removed from each hinge when the door is open.

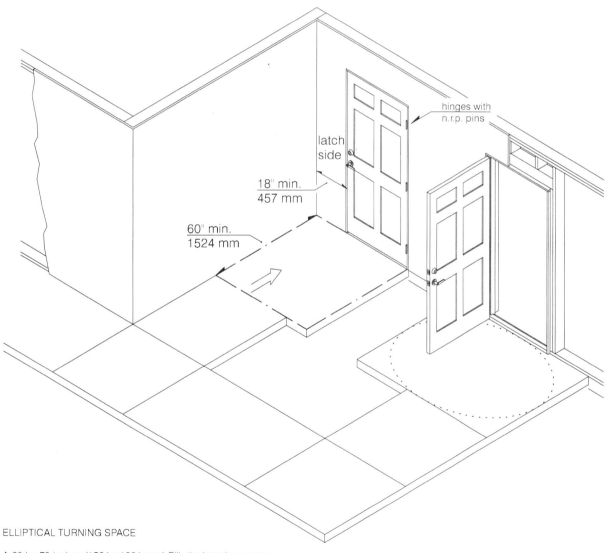

hinges with
n.r.p. pins

latch
side

18" min.
457 mm

60" min.
1524 mm

ELLIPTICAL TURNING SPACE

A 60 by 78 inches (1524 x 1981 mm) Elliptical turning space
is an easier space to turn around in than the Circular turning
space.

LATCH APPROACH - PUSH SIDE LANDING
   a. 42 inches (1067 mm) is the minimum width.
       48 inches (1219 mm) minimum if a closer is provided.
   b. 24 inches (610 mm) is the minimum clearance
       beyond the latch side.
   c. 60 inches (1524 mm) is the minimum depth
       when a ramp is attached.

When space permits, a turning space should be part of
an entry landing design. This is especially true when an
entry landing is attached to a ramp.

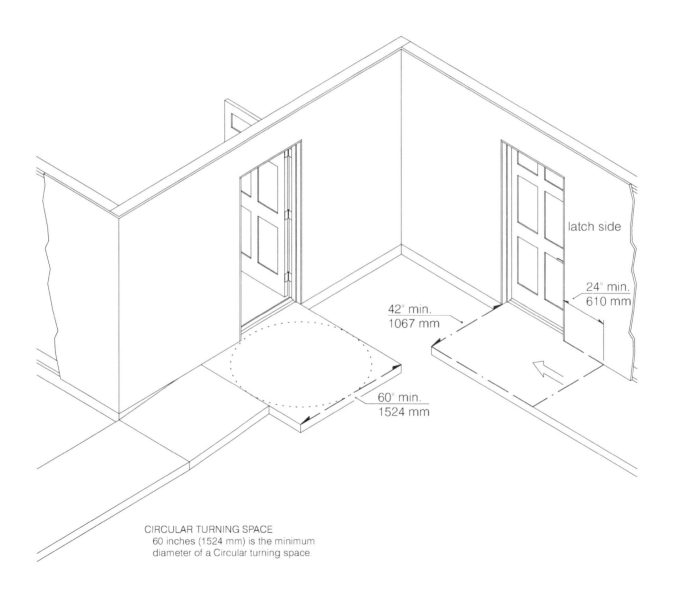

latch side

24" min.
610 mm

42" min.
1067 mm

60" min.
1524 mm

CIRCULAR TURNING SPACE
   60 inches (1524 mm) is the minimum
   diameter of a Circular turning space.

LATCH APPROACH - PULL SIDE LANDING
   a. 48 inches (1219 mm) is the minimum width.
       54 inches (1372 mm) minimum if a closer is provided.
   b. 24 inches (610 mm) is the minimum clearance
       beyond the latch side.
   c. 60 inches (1524 mm) is the minimum depth
       when a ramp is attached.

Security is a consideration. An exterior door swinging out
should have hinges with nonremovable (n.r.p.) pins.

Given the same swing out entrance door, a hinge or floor
mounted doorstop prevents the door from swinging out
of reach.

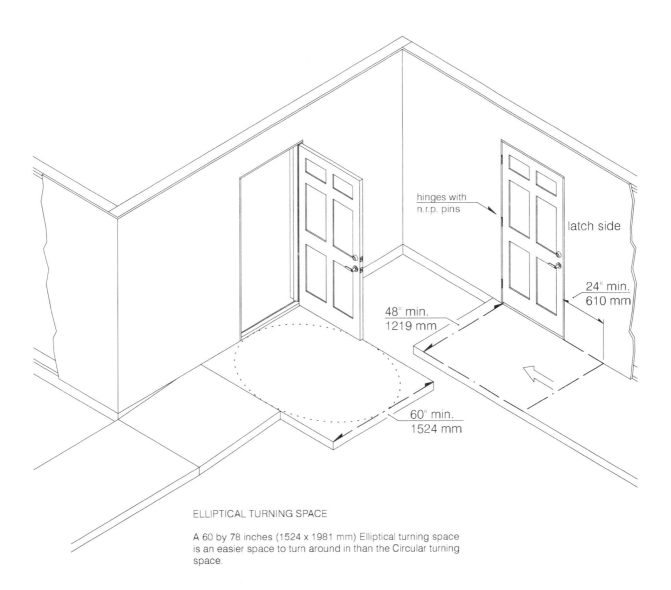

hinges with
n.r.p. pins

latch side

24" min.
610 mm

48" min.
1219 mm

60" min.
1524 mm

ELLIPTICAL TURNING SPACE

A 60 by 78 inches (1524 x 1981 mm) Elliptical turning space
is an easier space to turn around in than the Circular turning
space.

HINGE APPROACH - PUSH SIDE LANDING
    a. 42 inches (1067 mm) is the minimum width.
          48 inches (1219 mm) minimum if a closer and latch
          are provided.
    b. 22 inches (559 mm) is the minimum clearance
          beyond the hinge side.
    c. 60 inches (1524 mm) is the minimum depth
          when a ramp is attached.

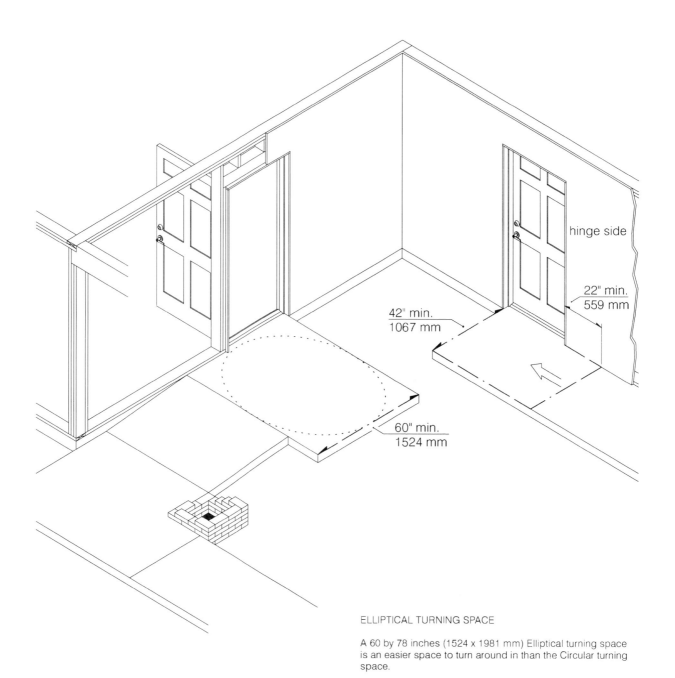

ELLIPTICAL TURNING SPACE

A 60 by 78 inches (1524 x 1981 mm) Elliptical turning space
is an easier space to turn around in than the Circular turning
space.

HINGE APPROACH - PULL SIDE LANDINGS

Landing One
- a. 60 inches (1524 mm) is the minimum width.
- b. 36 inches (914 mm) is the minimum clearance beyond the latch side.

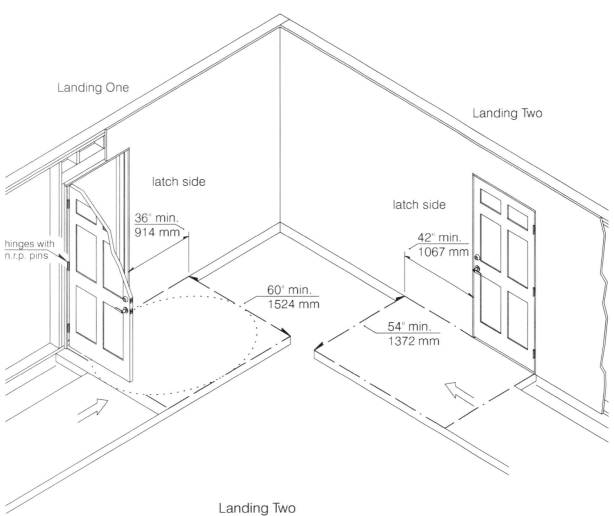

Landing One

Landing Two

latch side

36" min.
914 mm

latch side

42" min.
1067 mm

hinges with
n.r.p. pins

60" min.
1524 mm

54" min.
1372 mm

Landing Two
- a. 54 inches (1372 mm) is the minimum width.
- b. 42 inches (1067 mm) is the minimum clearance beyond the latch side.

NOTES

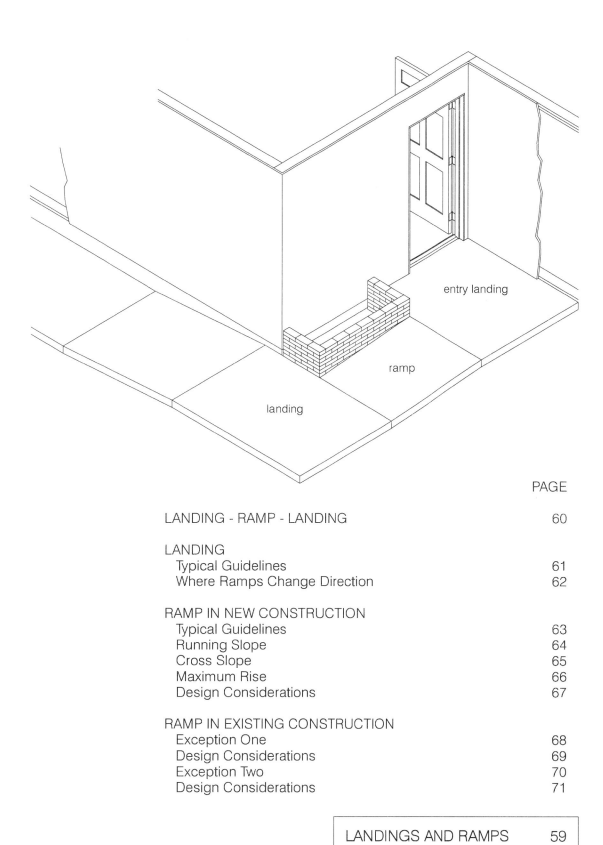

entry landing

ramp

landing

LANDING - RAMP - LANDING

There is a landing at the top and bottom of each ramp run.

Landings and ramps are firm, stable, slip resistant, and 1 : 48 is their maximum cross slope. Where they differ is in their running slopes.

- 1 : 48 is a landing's maximum running slope.
- 1 : 12 is a ramp's maximum running slope.
- An accessible route with a running slope steeper than 1 : 20 is a ramp.

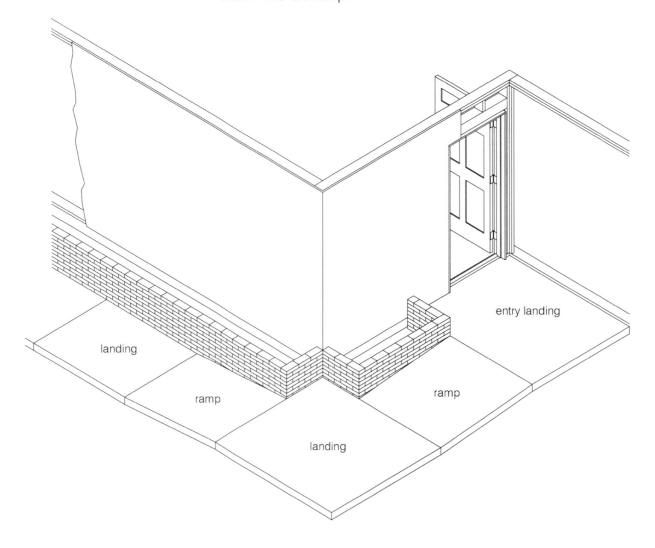

entry landing

landing

ramp

ramp

landing

LANDING
Typical Guidelines
a. 36 inches (914 mm) is the minimum width.
b. 60 inches (1524 mm) is the minimum depth.
c. There is a landing at the top and bottom of each ramp.
d. A landing is, at minimum, as wide as the widest ramp attached to it.
e. A landing has a maximum 1 : 48 cross slope and running slope.

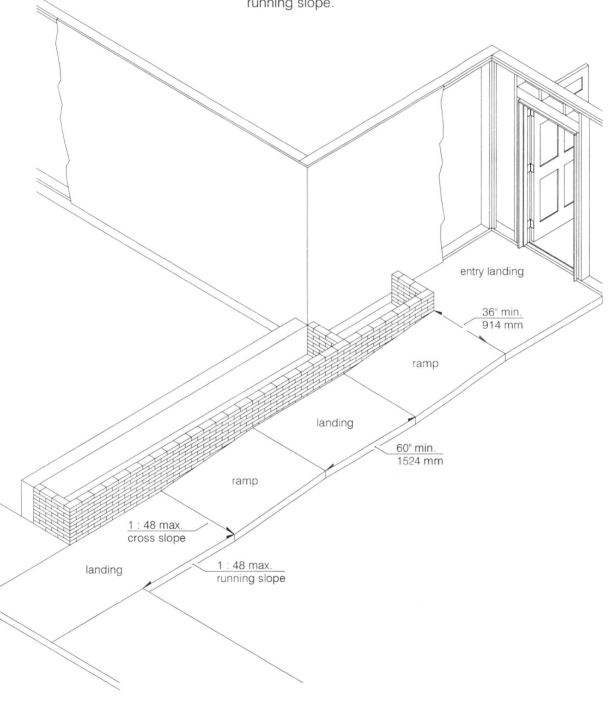

entry landing

36" min.
914 mm

ramp

landing

60" min.
1524 mm

ramp

landing

1 : 48 max.
cross slope

1 : 48 max.
running slope

LANDING
Where Ramps Change Direction
   a. 60 inches (1524 mm) is the minimum width.
   b. 60 inches (1524 mm) is the minimum depth.
   c. A landing has a maximum 1 : 48 cross slope
       and running slope.

A 60 inch by 60 inch landing can be a turning space.
Inside that minimum turning space, a 180 degree turn
will require thought and care.

Wherever space permits, minimum widths and depths
should be increased in size. Note that the landings and
ramps on the next page are wider than the minimum widths
illustrated below.

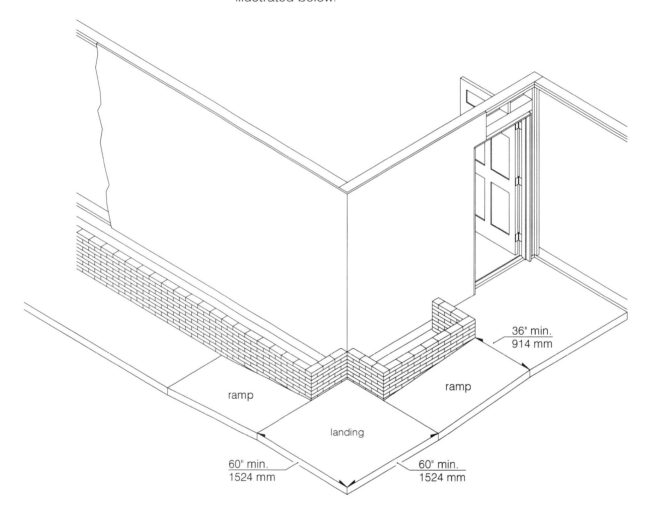

RAMP IN NEW CONSTRUCTION
  Typical Guidelines
      a. 36 inches (914 mm) is the minimum width.
      b. 1 : 48 is the maximum cross slope.
      c. An accessible route with a running slope steeper
          than 1 : 20 is a ramp.
      d. 1 : 12 is the maximum running slope.
      e. Must have an accessible change in level.
      f. A ramp with a rise greater than 6 inches (152 mm)
          requires handrails.
      g. 30 inches (762 mm) is the maximum rise of a
          single ramp run.

Note: In existing construction, when space limitations do not
permit a 1 : 12 ramp, there are two exceptions. The exceptions
are on pages 68 and 70.

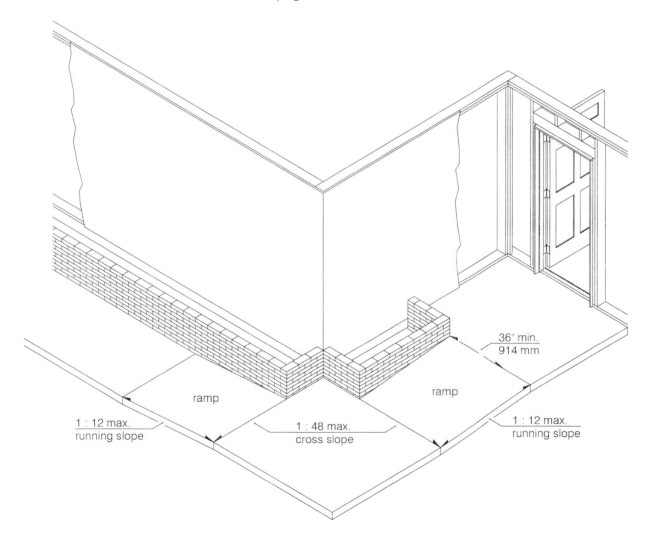

36" min.
914 mm

ramp

ramp

1 : 12 max.
running slope

1 : 48 max.
cross slope

1 : 12 max.
running slope

RAMP IN NEW CONSTRUCTION
Running Slope
     a. An accessible route with a running slope steeper than
          1 : 20 is a ramp.
     b. 1 : 12 is the maximum running slope of a ramp
          in new construction.

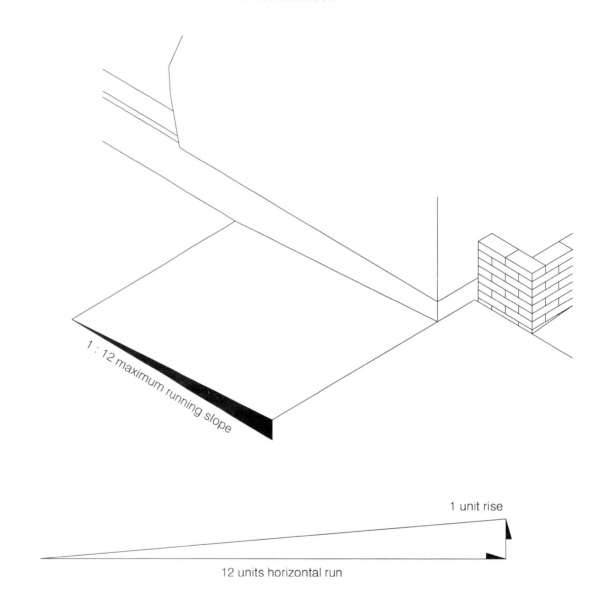

1 : 12 rise and corresponding run

1" (25.4 mm) rise = 12" (305 mm) horizontal run	4" (101.6 mm) rise = 48" (1219 mm) horizontal run
2" (50.8 mm) rise = 24" (610 mm) horizontal run	6" (152 mm) rise = 72" (1829 mm) horizontal run
3" (76.2 mm) rise = 36" (914 mm) horizontal run	30" (762 mm) rise = 30' (9.14 m) horizontal run

RAMP IN NEW CONSTRUCTION
Cross Slope
    1 : 48 is the maximum cross slope of a ramp.

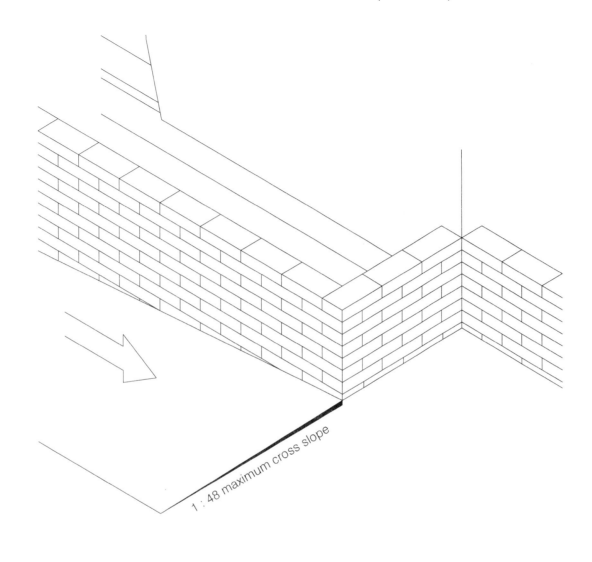

1 : 48 maximum cross slope

1 unit rise

48 units horizontal run

1 : 48 rise and corresponding run

3/4" (19.1 mm) rise = 36" (914 mm) horizontal run	1-1/8" (28.6 mm) rise = 54" (1372 mm) horizontal run
7/8" (22.2 mm) rise = 42" (1067 mm) horizontal run	1-1/4" (31.8 mm) rise = 60" (1524 mm) horizontal run
1" (25.4 mm) rise = 48" (1219 mm) horizontal run	1-1/2" (38.1 mm) rise = 72" (1829 mm) horizontal run

RAMP IN NEW CONSTRUCTION
Maximum Rise
    a. 30 inches (762 mm) is the maximum rise
        of a single ramp run.
    b. A ramp with a rise greater than 6 inches (152 mm)
        requires handrails that comply with a locality's
        building standards.

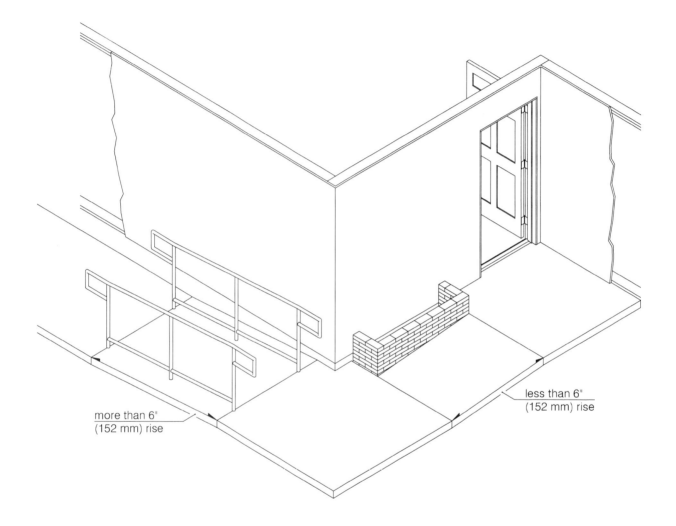

more than 6"
(152 mm) rise

less than 6"
(152 mm) rise

Four components make up a running slope.
    1. A running slope has a two unit designation such as 1 : 12.
    2. The first number is the vertical change in height, always
        1 unit.
    3. The second number is the horizontal distance in like units.
    4. As the second number becomes larger, the slope becomes
        flatter.

Example: 1 : 20 is a flatter slope than 1 : 12.

RAMP IN NEW CONSTRUCTION
Design Considerations

Ramp length is a consideration, especially for a building
project with a tight budget. A long ramp with a rise of more
than 6 inches (152 mm) will require handrails to facilitate
the climb. There are ways to avoid the expense of handrails.

One alternative is two short ramps with a landing in-between to
break up the climb. A second alternative is a flatter, less tiring
route with a running slope of 1 : 20 or less.

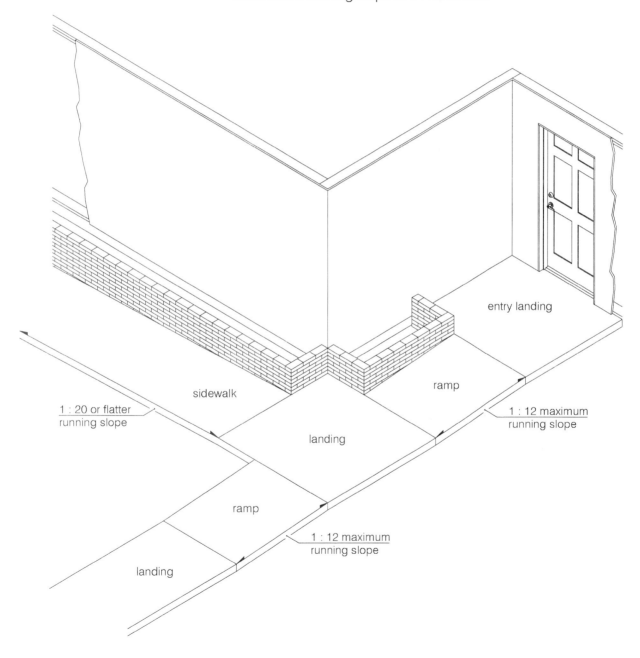

entry landing

sidewalk

ramp

1 : 20 or flatter
running slope

1 : 12 maximum
running slope

landing

ramp

1 : 12 maximum
running slope

landing

RAMP IN EXISTING CONSTRUCTION
Exception One
In existing construction, when space limitations do not permit
a 1 : 12 ramp, a ramp with a 1 : 12 to 1 : 10 running slope is
permitted provided its rise does not exceed 6 inches (152 mm).

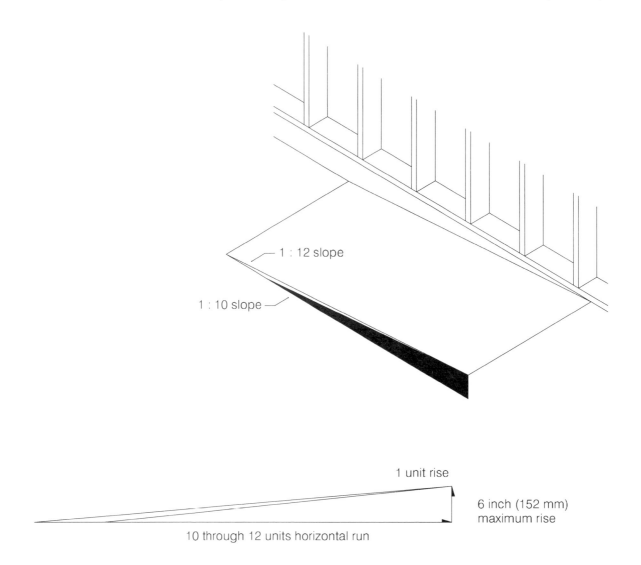

1 : 12 slope

1 : 10 slope

1 unit rise

6 inch (152 mm)
maximum rise

10 through 12 units horizontal run

1 : 12 rise and corresponding run

1"	(25.4 mm) rise = 12"	(305 mm)	horizontal run
2"	(50.8 mm) rise = 24"	(610 mm)	horizontal run
3"	(76.2 mm) rise = 36"	(914 mm)	horizontal run
4"	(101.6 mm) rise = 48"	(1219 mm)	horizontal run
5"	(127 mm) rise = 60"	(1524 mm)	horizontal run
6"	(152 mm) rise = 72"	(1829 mm)	horizontal run

1 : 10 rise and corresponding run

1"	(25.4 mm) rise = 10"	(254 mm)	horizontal run
2"	(50.8 mm) rise = 20"	(508 mm)	horizontal run
3"	(76.2 mm) rise = 30"	(762 mm)	horizontal run
4"	(101.6 mm) rise = 40"	(1016 mm)	horizontal run
5"	(127 mm) rise = 50"	(1270 mm)	horizontal run
6"	(152 mm) rise = 60"	(1524 mm)	horizontal run

RAMP IN EXISTING CONSTRUCTION
  Design Considerations

Because a ramp inside a home requires a significant
length of unobstructed floor space, an interior route with
a landing-ramp-landing combination is a major design
decision.

In all cases, 36 inches (914 mm) is the minimum width of a
ramp. A landing must be as wide as the widest ramp attached
to it, and 60 inches (1524 mm) is a landing's minimum depth.

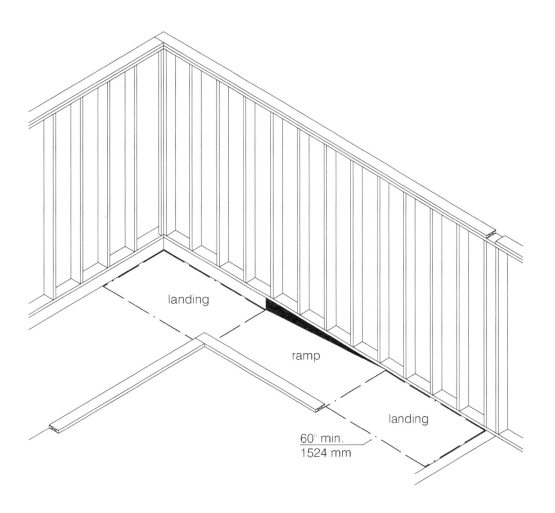

landing

ramp

landing

60" min.
1524 mm

RAMP IN EXISTING CONSTRUCTION
Exception Two
In existing construction, when space limitations do not permit a 1 : 12 ramp, a ramp with a 1 : 10 to 1 : 8 running slope is permitted provided its rise does not exceed 3 inches (76.2 mm). A ramp steeper than 1 : 8 is prohibited.

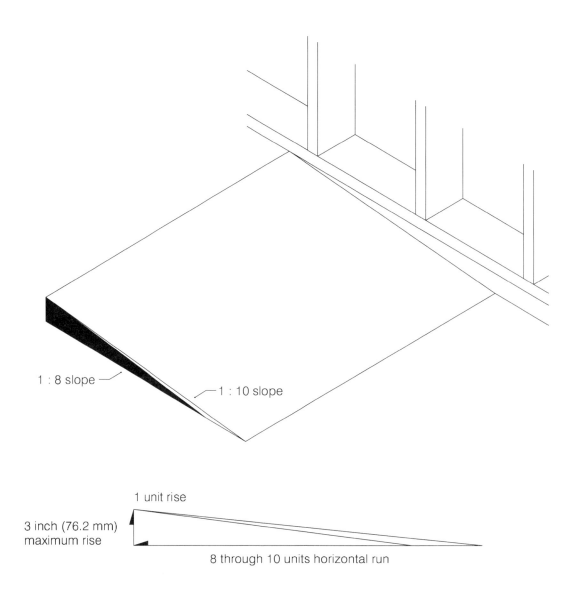

1 : 8 slope

1 : 10 slope

1 unit rise

3 inch (76.2 mm) maximum rise

8 through 10 units horizontal run

1 : 10 rise and corresponding run

1:8 rise and corresponding run

1 : 10 rise and corresponding run	1:8 rise and corresponding run
1" (25.4 mm) rise = 10" (254 mm) horizontal run	1" (25.4 mm) rise = 8" (203 mm) horizontal run
2" (50.8 mm) rise = 20" (508 mm) horizontal run	2" (50.8 mm) rise = 16" (406 mm) horizontal run
3" (76.2 mm) rise = 30" (762 mm) horizontal run	3" (76.2 mm) rise = 24" (610 mm) horizontal run

RAMP IN EXISTING CONSTRUCTION
  Design Considerations

Because a ramp inside a home requires a significant
length of unobstructed floor space, an interior route with
a landing-ramp-landing combination is a major design
decision.

In all cases, 36 inches (914 mm) is the minimum width of a
ramp. A landing must be as wide as the widest ramp attached
to it, and 60 inches (1524 mm) is a landing's minimum depth.

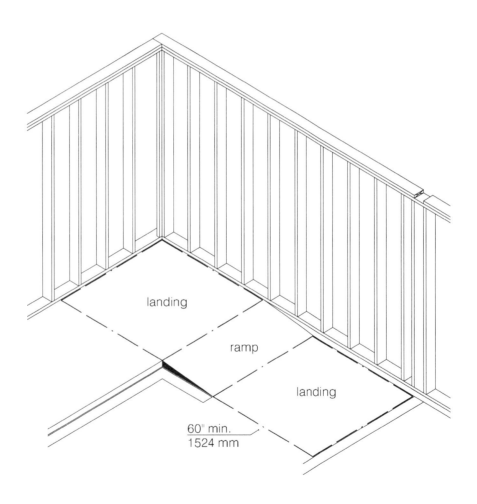

NOTES

REACH, APPROACH, AND EGRESS

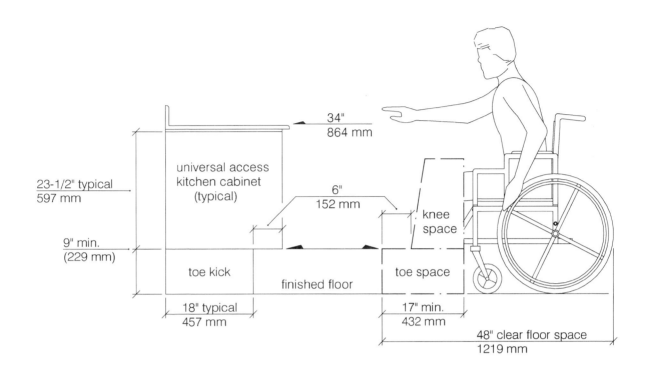

34"
864 mm

universal access
kitchen cabinet
(typical)

6"
152 mm

knee
space

23-1/2" typical
597 mm

9" min.
(229 mm)

toe kick

finished floor

toe space

18" typical
457 mm

17" min.
432 mm

48" clear floor space
1219 mm

REACH AND APPROACH DIRECTION

High and low reach have an approach direction.

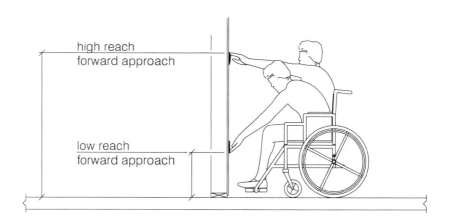

high reach
forward approach

low reach
forward approach

A forward approach (hand is forward) is illustrated above.
A parallel approach (hand to the side) is illustrated below.

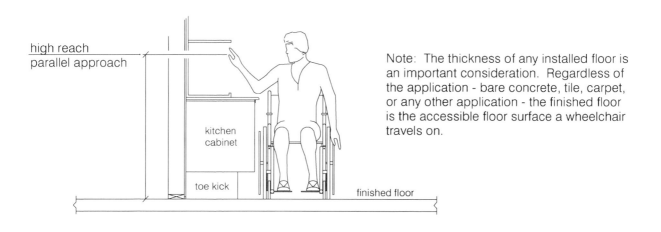

high reach
parallel approach

kitchen
cabinet

toe kick

finished floor

Note: The thickness of any installed floor is an important consideration. Regardless of the application - bare concrete, tile, carpet, or any other application - the finished floor is the accessible floor surface a wheelchair travels on.

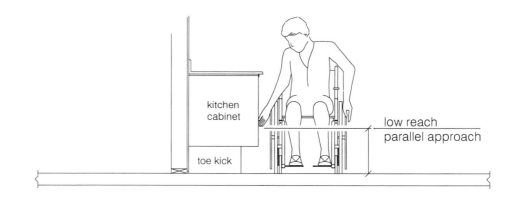

kitchen
cabinet

toe kick

low reach
parallel approach

REACH AND OBSTRUCTIONS

Obstructions play a role in limiting reach.

When reaching over an obstruction, using a parallel approach, there are two limiting factors.
1. An obstruction's depth is one limiting factor.
2. An obstruction's height above the finished floor is the second.

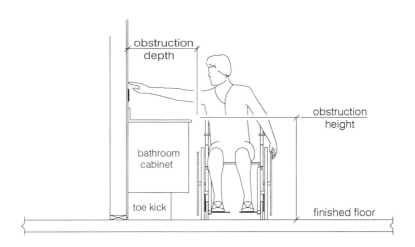

When reaching over an obstruction, using a forward approach, there are three limiting factors.
1. Obstruction's depth.
2. Kitchen work surface's maximum height, page 216.
3. Knee clearance below a fixture, page 132.

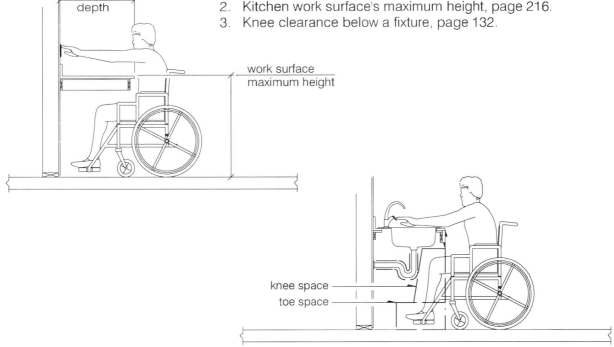

FORWARD APPROACH
Unobstructed
High forward reach
48 inches (1219 mm) is the maximum unobstructed high forward reach above the finished floor.

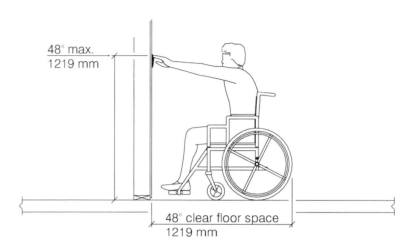

48" max.
1219 mm

48" clear floor space
1219 mm

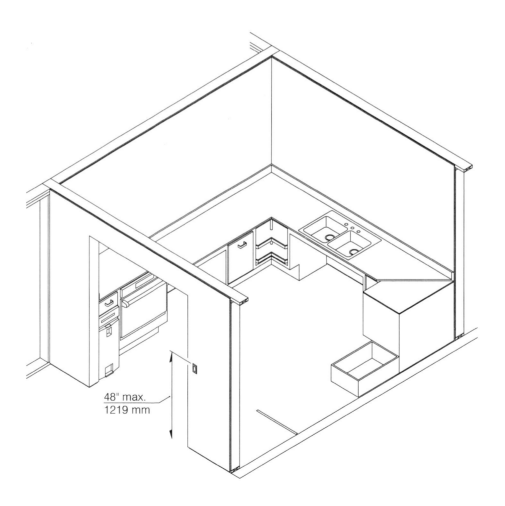

48" max.
1219 mm

FORWARD APPROACH
  Unobstructed
    Low forward reach
      15 inches (381 mm) is the minimum unobstructed
      low forward reach above the finished floor.

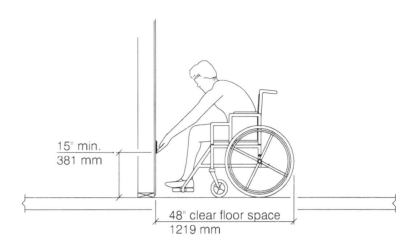

15" min.
381 mm

48" clear floor space
1219 mm

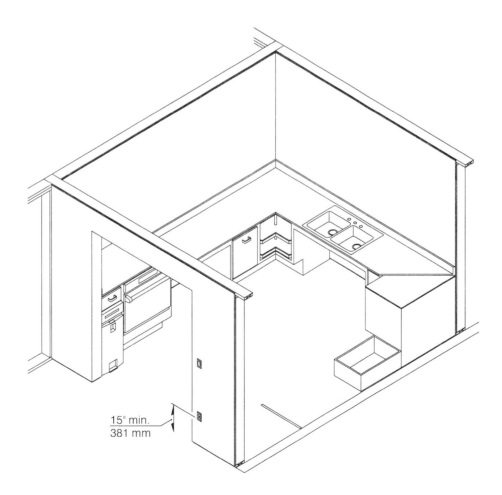

15" min.
381 mm

FORWARD APPROACH
  Obstructed High Forward Reach
    Option one
      44 inches (1118 mm) is the maximum high forward reach
      over an obstruction more than 20 inches to 25 inches
      (508 - 635 mm) maximum in depth.

Note: A kitchen's work surface has a minimum width and a
maximum height of 34 inches (864 mm) above the finished
floor. Its depth is typically 25 to 25-1/2 inches (635 - 648 mm).

* Receptacles and switches are approximately 1/2" (12.7 mm)
  in depth, leaving the spirit of accessibility intact with the
  25 inch forward reach.

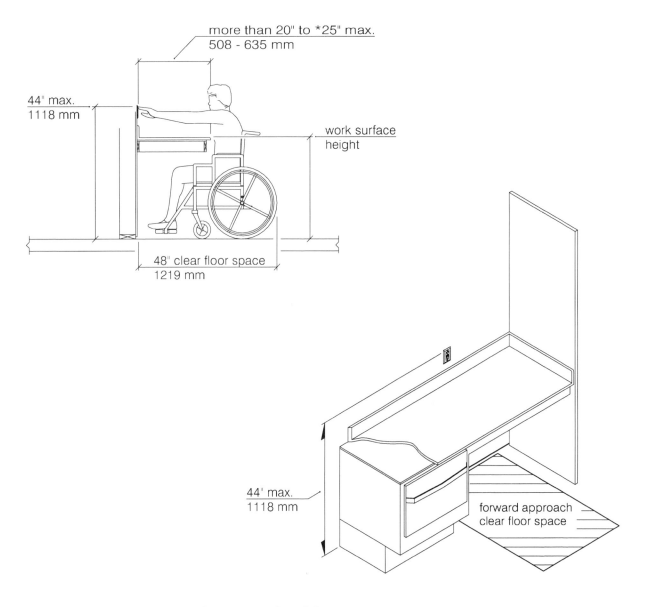

more than 20" to *25" max.
508 - 635 mm

44" max.
1118 mm

work surface
height

48" clear floor space
1219 mm

44" max.
1118 mm

forward approach
clear floor space

FORWARD APPROACH
  Obstructed High Forward Reach
    Option two
      48 inches (1219 mm) is the maximum
      high forward reach over an obstruction
      20 inches (508 mm) maximum in depth.

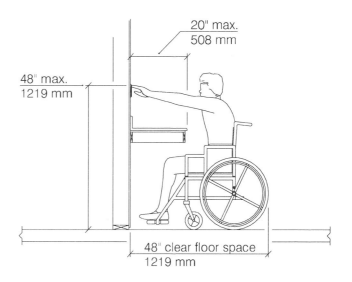

20" max.
508 mm

48" max.
1219 mm

48" clear floor space
1219 mm

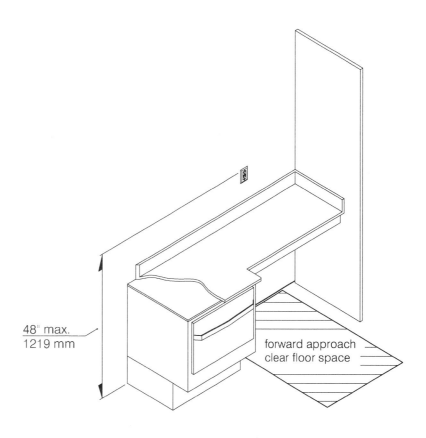

48" max.
1219 mm

forward approach
clear floor space

PARALLEL APPROACH
  Unobstructed
    High parallel reach
      48 inches (1219 mm) is the maximum unobstructed
      high parallel reach above the finished floor.

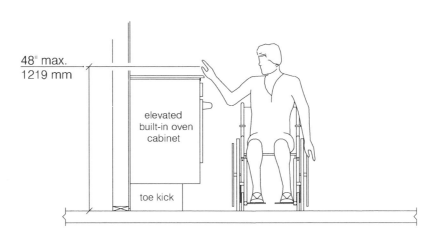

48" max.
1219 mm

elevated
built-in oven
cabinet

toe kick

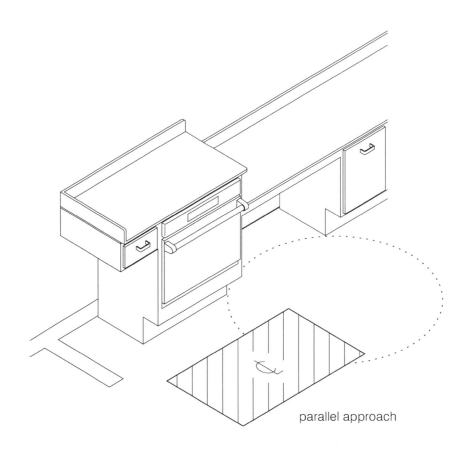

parallel approach

PARALLEL APPROACH
  Unobstructed
    Low parallel reach
      15 inches (381 mm) is the minimum unobstructed
      low parallel reach above the finished floor.

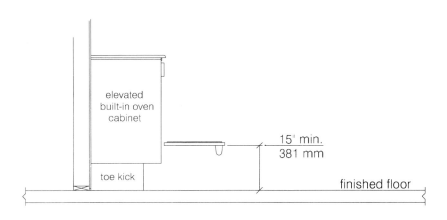

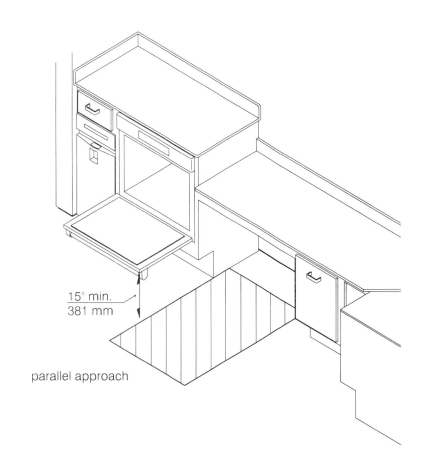

parallel approach

PARALLEL APPROACH
  Obstructed High Parallel Reach
    Option one
      46 inches (1168 mm) is the maximum high parallel reach
      over an obstruction more than 10 inches to
      24 inches (254 - 610 mm) maximum in depth and
      34 inches (864 mm) maximum above the finished floor.

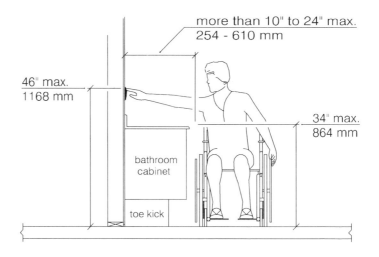

Note: The thickness of any installed floor is an important
consideration. Regardless of the application - bare concrete,
tile, carpet, or any other application - the finished floor is the
accessible floor surface a wheelchair travels on.

A typical universal access bathroom cabinet is pictured below.

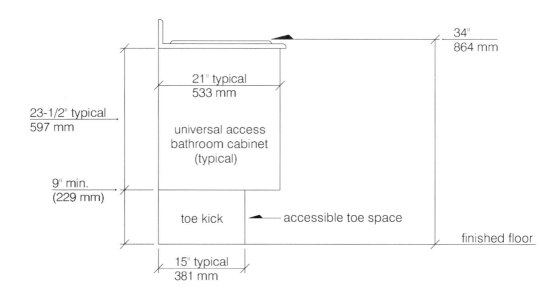

PARALLEL APPROACH
  Obstructed High Parallel Reach
    Option two
      48 inches (1219 mm) is the maximum high parallel reach
      10 inches (254 mm) maximum beyond an obstruction
      34 inches (864 mm) maximum above the finished floor.

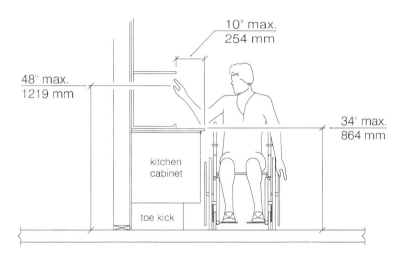

Note: For a sweeping turn to take advantage of an accessible toe space under a cabinet, the cabinet must be 9 inches minimum above the finished floor.

Below, a universal access kitchen cabinet has a 1/2 inch (12.7 mm) plywood cap and a 3/4 inch (19.05 mm) countertop. 34 inches to the top of the sink is illustrated.

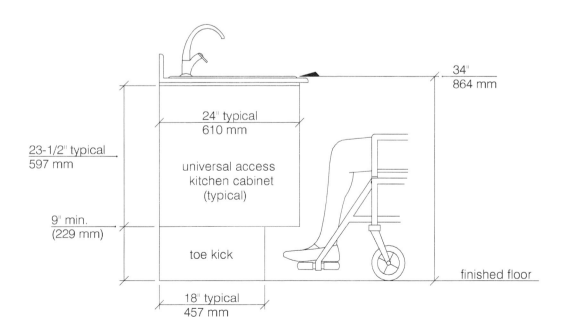

HIGH AND LOW REACH AND VIEW

High and low reach are considerations throughout the house.
A front loading washer and a front loading dryer are two examples.

Provided that the controls are no higher than 48 inches (1219 mm)
above the finished floor, both a washer and a dryer should be
elevated to a point where wet or dry clothes are accessible.
The appliance door should also swing sideways, allowing
a close parallel approach.

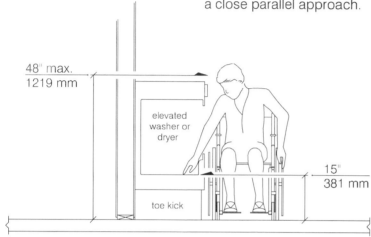

A mirror's lower edge, above the finished floor, is another
consideration. 40 inches (1016 mm) is its maximum height
when it is above a lavatory or countertop. 35 inches (889 mm)
is the lower edge's maximum height when it is not.

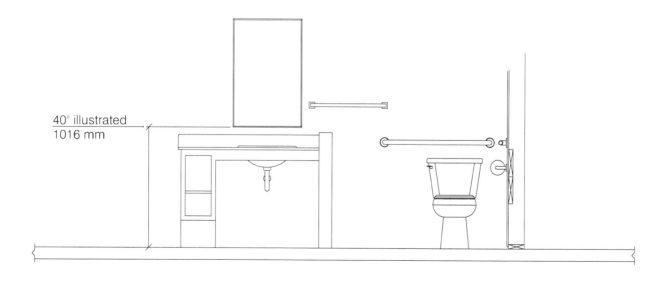

EGRESS

Each residential bedroom must have a means of emergency-egress that complies with a locality's building standards.

Wheelchair accessibility, at a residential home's first floor, asks that an emergency-egress receive special consideration. A 3068 hinged doorway is illustrated below.

- 30 is shorthand for 3 feet and 0 inches in width (914 mm).
- 68 is shorthand for 6 feet and 8 inches in height (2032 mm).

Note: An exterior door swinging out should have hinges with nonremovable (n.r.p.) pins. To remove the pins, a retaining screw must be removed from each hinge when the door is open.

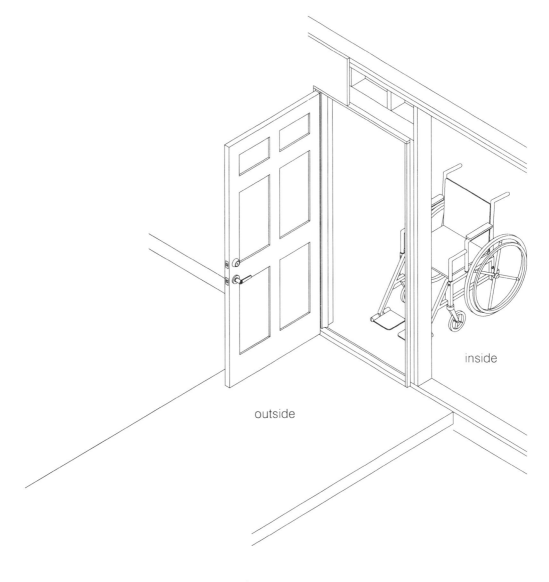

inside

outside

NOTES

INTERIOR LANDINGS

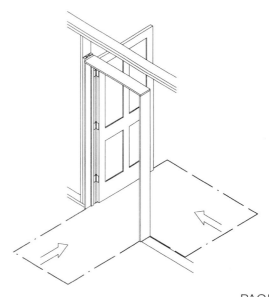

PAGE

DESIGN CONSIDERATIONS

An accessible doorway has a floor space on either side
called a landing. Landings are firm, stable, slip resistant,
and 1 : 48 is the maximum cross slope and running slope.

A landing on each side of a doorway or a passageway is
a constant. It is a landing's size that is variable.

HINGED DOOR

32 inches (813 mm) is the minimum width between
door and doorstop when the door is open 90 degrees.

32" min.
813 mm

hinge side   latch side

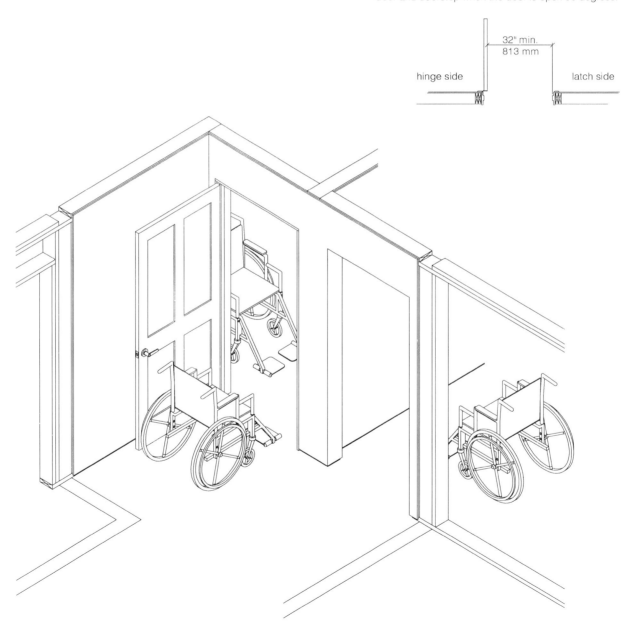

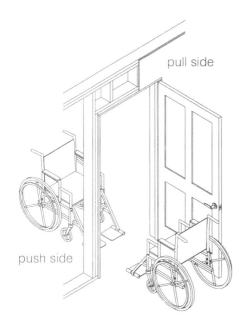

pull side

push side

Given the full width of an accessible doorway, landing considerations are:

Approach and Hardware Location
　　Does a doorway have a forward approach?
　　Does a doorway have a latch approach?
　　Does a doorway have a hinge approach?

Door Swing
　　Does a door push open?
　　Does a door pull open?

Clearance Parallel to Doorway
　　Does a doorway have clearance beyond the latch side or beyond the hinge side?

Closer
　　Does a door have a closer?

Ramp
　　Is a ramp attached to the landing? Examples are on pages 69 and 71.

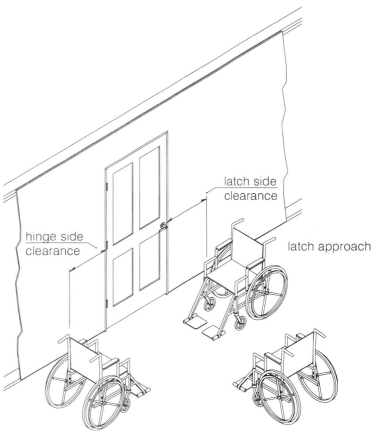

latch side clearance

hinge side clearance

latch approach

hinge approach

forward approach

FRONT APPROACH - PUSH SIDE LANDING
   a. 12 inches (305 mm) is the minimum clearance
      beyond the latch side if a closer and latch are provided.
   b. 48 inches (1219 mm) is the minimum depth.
   c. 60 inches (1524 mm) is the minimum depth
      when a ramp is attached.

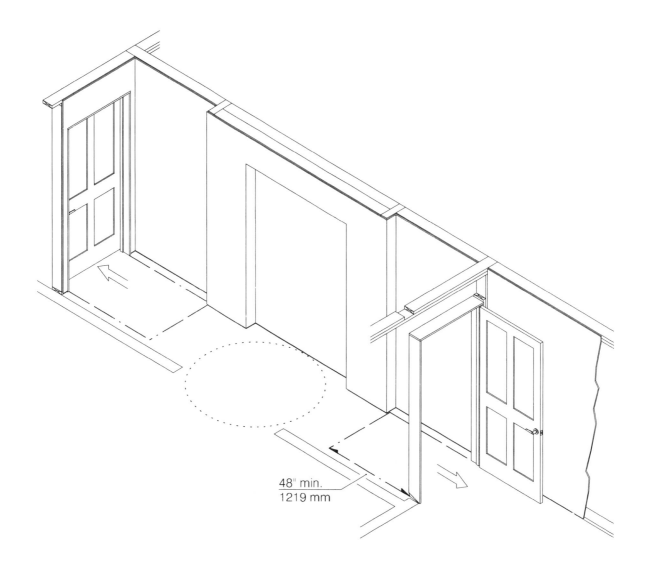

48" min.
1219 mm

Note: A landing with a minimum depth assumes the possibility
of an obstruction. In this section, the pop-out details on the
hallway walls represent an obstruction on the borderline of
an interior landing.

FRONT APPROACH - PULL SIDE LANDING
  a. 18 inches (457 mm) is the minimum clearance
      beyond the latch side.
  b. 60 inches (1524 mm) is the minimum depth.

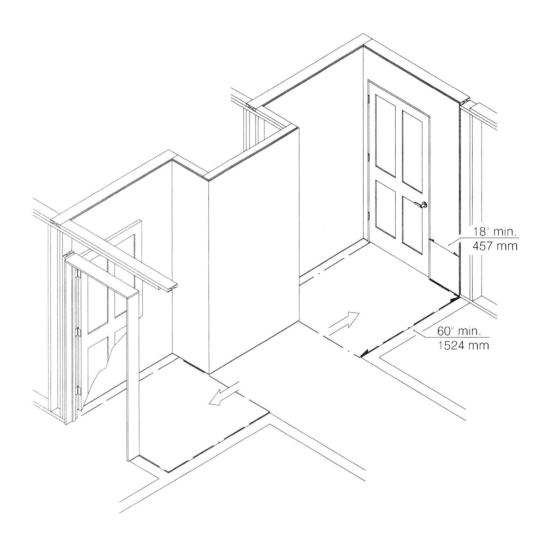

18" min.
457 mm

60" min.
1524 mm

The landing on the other side of the example above is a
push-side landing. The approach to that landing may be
determined by a fixture's location, furniture arrangement
near the door, or the like.

LATCH APPROACH - PUSH SIDE LANDING
   a. 42 inches (1067 mm) is the minimum width.
       48 inches (1219 mm) minimum if a closer is provided.
   b. 24 inches (610 mm) is the minimum clearance
       beyond the latch side.
   c. 60 inches (1524 mm) is the minimum depth
       when a ramp is attached.

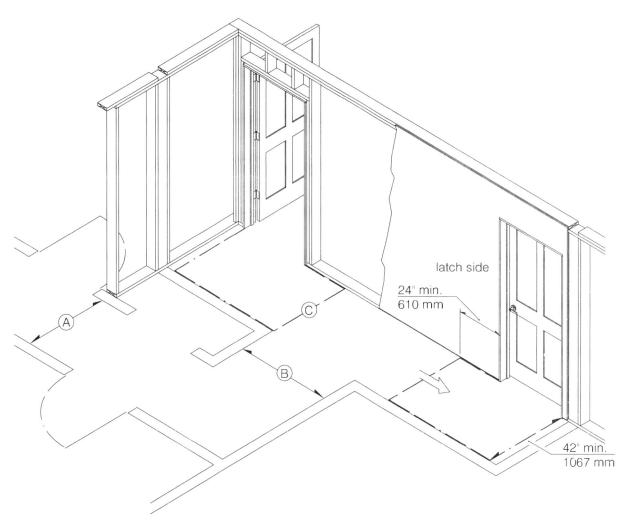

The path to an interior landing may require a turn inside a hallway.
The picture above details the mechanics of turn one's 90 degree
turns.

   Turn One
      When the distance between two 90 degree turns is less than
      48 inches (1219 mm), if routes A and C are 42 inches (1067 mm)
      minimum in width, 48 inches is the minimum width of route B.

LATCH APPROACH - PULL SIDE LANDING
- a. 48 inches (1219 mm) is the minimum width.
  54 inches (1372 mm) minimum if a closer is provided.
- b. 24 inches (610 mm) is the minimum clearance beyond the latch side.
- c. 60 inches (1524 mm) is the minimum depth when a ramp is attached.

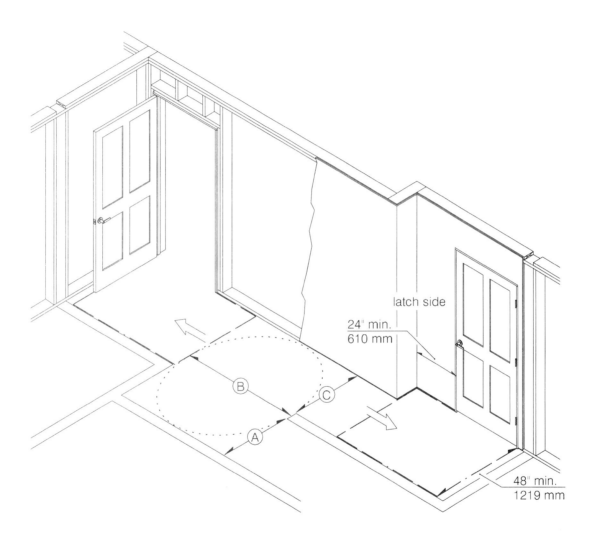

The path to an interior landing may require a turn inside a hallway. The picture above details the mechanics of turn two's 90 degree turns.

Turn Two
   When the distance between two 90 degree turns is less than 48 inches (1219 mm), if routes A and C are 36 inches (914 mm) minimum in width, 60 inches (1524 mm) is the minimum width of route B.

HINGE APPROACH - PUSH SIDE LANDING
  a. 42 inches (1067 mm) is the minimum width.
      48 inches (1219 mm) minimum if a closer and latch
      are provided.
  b. 22 inches (559 mm) is the minimum clearance
      beyond the hinge side.
  c. 60 inches (1524 mm) is the minimum depth
      when a ramp is attached.

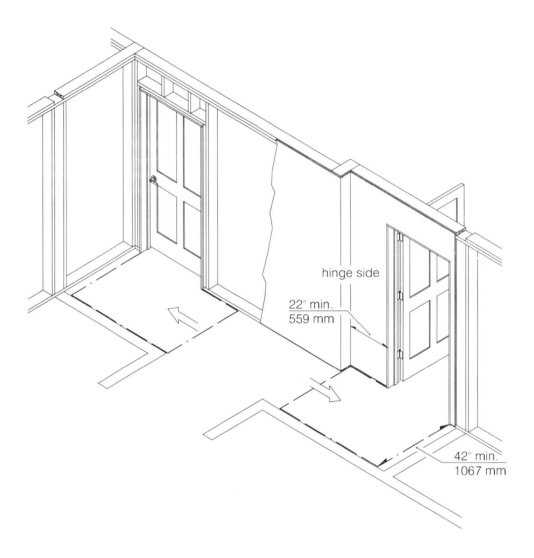

The landing on the other side of the example above is a
pull-side landing. The approach to that landing may be
determined by an obstruction, a fixture, furniture near the
door, or the like.

HINGE APPROACH - PULL SIDE LANDINGS

Landing One
  a. 60 inches (1524 mm) is the minimum width.
  b. 36 inches (914 mm) is the minimum clearance beyond the latch side.

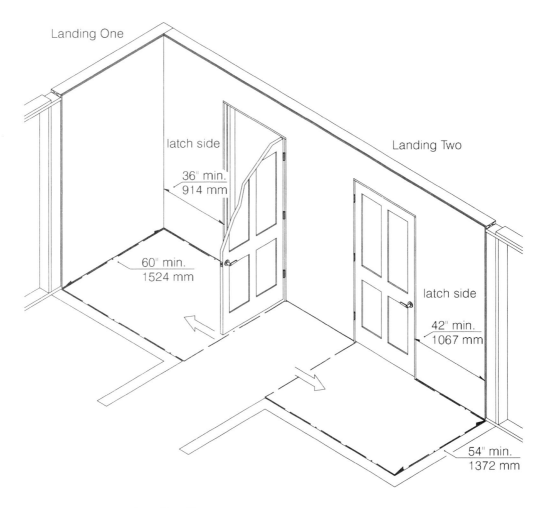

Landing Two
  a. 54 inches (1372 mm) is the minimum width.
  b. 42 inches (1067 mm) is the minimum clearance beyond the latch side.

OVERLAPPING LANDINGS
  Where Doors Swing Away From Each Other
    48 inches (1219 mm) is the minimum depth between
    doorways.

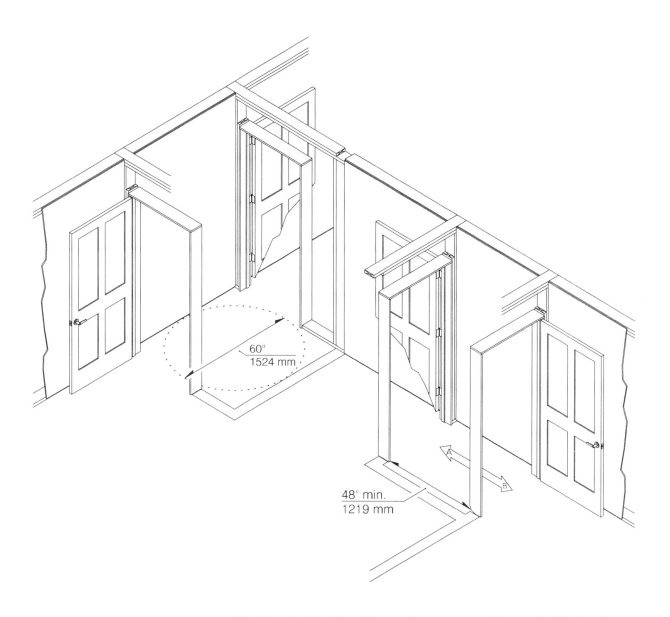

60"
1524 mm

48" min.
1219 mm

A

B

The door in direction A has a front approach - push side landing.
The door in direction B has a front approach - push side landing.

OVERLAPPING LANDINGS
Where Doors Swing in the Same Direction
a. 18 inches (457 mm) is the minimum clearance beyond the latch of the pull - side door.
b. 48 inches (1219 mm) and the length of the pull - side door open at 90 degrees is the minimum depth between doorways.

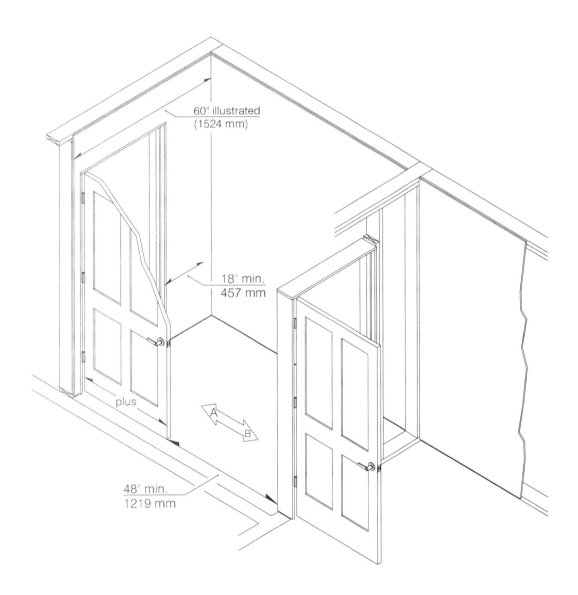

60" illustrated
(1524 mm)

18" min.
457 mm

plus

48" min.
1219 mm

The door in direction A has a front approach - pull side landing.
The door in direction B has a front approach - push side landing.

PASSAGEWAY LANDINGS

At an accessible passageway less than 36 inches (914 mm) wide:

Forward Approach Landing
a. Width - See passageway width note below.
b. 48 inches (1219 mm) is the minimum depth.

Parallel Approach Landing
a. 42 inches (1067 mm) is the minimum width.
b. 24 inches (610 mm) of clearance on the approach side is illustrated.

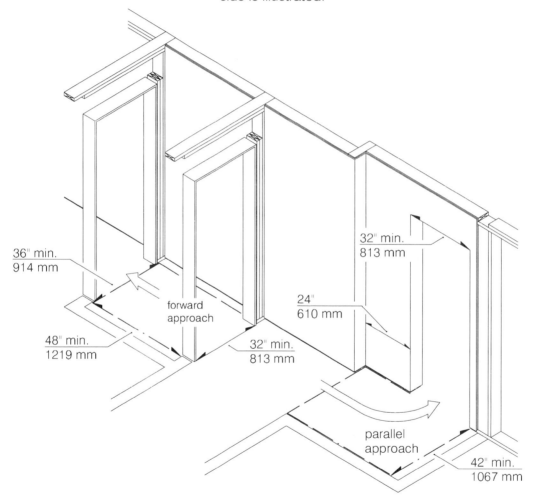

Passageway width note:
a. 36 inches (914 mm) is the minimum width of passageway more than 24 inches (610 mm) in depth.
b. 32 inches (813 mm) is the minimum width of a passageway 24 inches (610 mm) or less in depth. Consecutive 32 inch wide segments must have a 36 x 48 inch (914 x 1219 mm) unobstructed floor space separating them.

POCKET DOOR LANDINGS
Front Approach
48 inches (1219 mm) is the minimum depth.

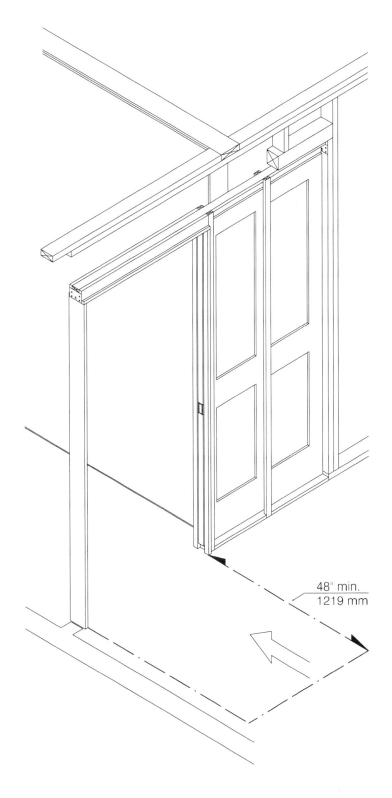

48" min.
1219 mm

POCKET DOOR LANDINGS
Latch Approach
a. 42 inches (1067 mm) is the minimum width.
b. 24 inches (610 mm) is the minimum clearance beyond the latch side.
c. 60 inches (1524 mm) is the minimum depth when a ramp is attached.

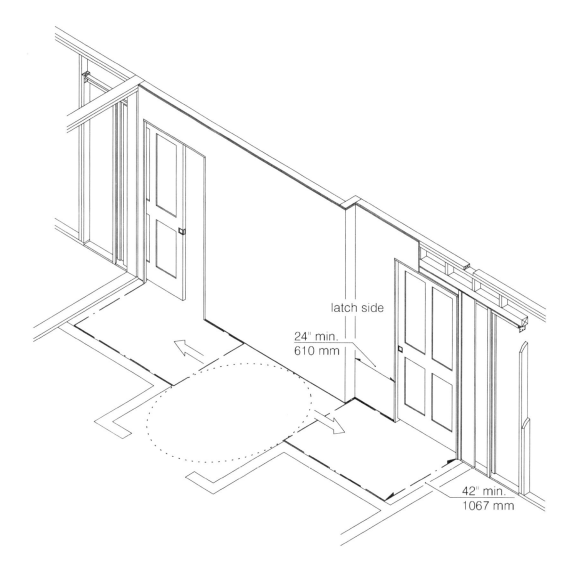

latch side

24" min.
610 mm

42" min.
1067 mm

ELLIPTICAL TURNING SPACE

A 60 by 78 inches (1524 x 1981 mm) Elliptical turning space is an easier space to turn around in than the Circular turning space.

POCKET DOOR LANDINGS
  Pocket Approach
      a. 42 inches (1067 mm) is the minimum width.
      b. 22 inches (559 mm) is the minimum clearance
          beyond the pocket side.
      c. 60 inches (1524 mm) is the minimum depth
          when a ramp is attached.

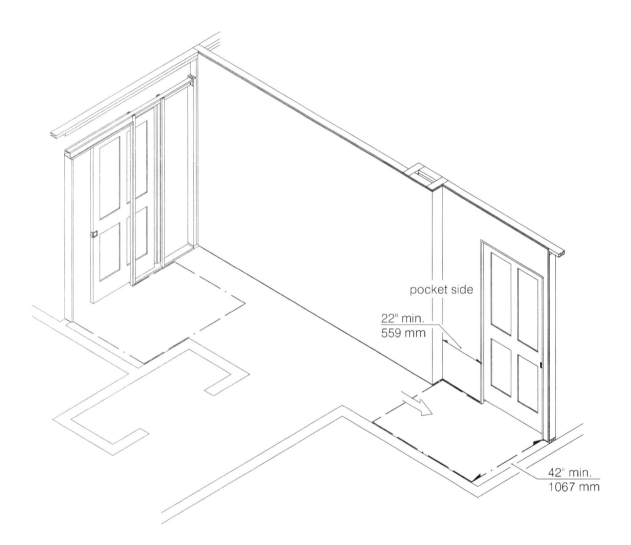

pocket side

22" min.
559 mm

42" min.
1067 mm

A pocket door has advantages.
  ▪ Door swing is eliminated.
  ▪ Landing size on both sides of the door can be kept to a
    minimum.

A pocket door has disadvantages.
  ▪ The latch is small and hard to grasp.
  ▪ The frame requires twice the wall space as a hinged door.

HALLWAYS

A hinged door swinging away from a hallway has a
push - side landing.

A hinged door swinging into a hallway has a pull - side
landing.

1. Front approach - Push side
2. Front approach - Pull side
3. Latch approach - Push side
4. Latch approach - Pull side
5. Hinge approach - Push side
6. Hinge approach - Pull side,
   landing one

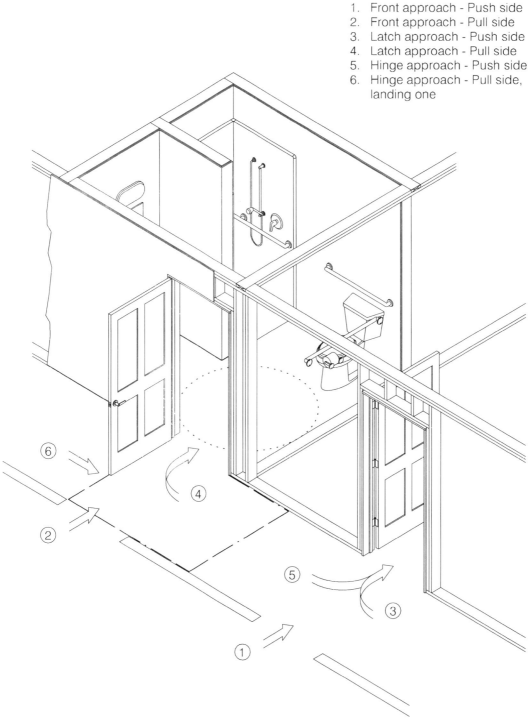

LANDING NOTES

- A doorway or a passageway has a landing on either side.

- A doorway or a passageway has a forward approach or a parallel approach.

- A landing's width and depth have several determining factors. Approach direction, hardware location, and door swing are only three of the considerations.

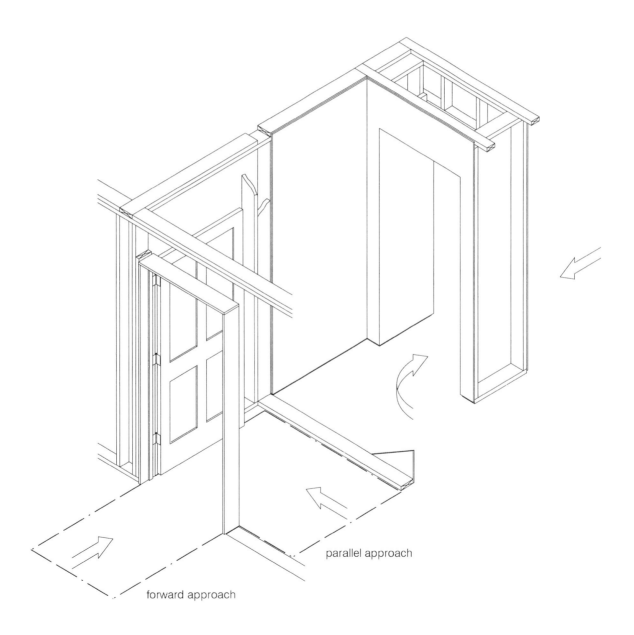

parallel approach

forward approach

NOTES

RESIDENTIAL BATHROOMS

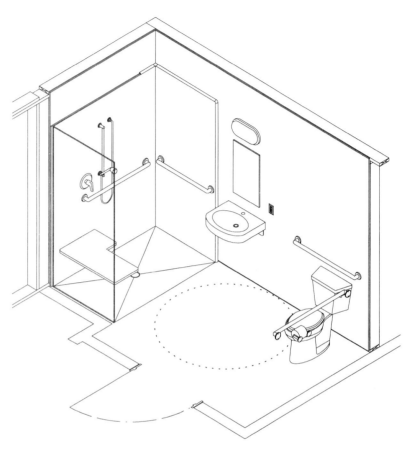

TYPICAL BATHROOM
Access Problems

When wheelchair access is part of a bathroom plan, every path, space, and fixture requires special consideration. Below is a typical bathroom with wheelchair access problems.

- The bathroom has a 2468 door, a door with approximately 25-1/2 inches (749 mm) between door and doorstop when the door is open 90 degrees.
   24 is shorthand for 2 feet and 4 inches in width (711 mm).
   68 is shorthand for 6 feet and 8 inches in height (2032 mm).

- The bathroom has a water closet next to a bathtub.

- The bathroom has a cabinet, countertop and sink.

Inside this typical bathroom a person cannot wheel in, use each fixture, turn around and leave.

TYPICAL BATHROOM

BATHTUB
1 - 30 inch by 60 inch
   (762 x 1524 mm)
   Bathtub

1 - Bathtub/shower controls

1 - Bathtub water spout

1 - Showerhead

WATER CLOSET
1 - Water closet

1 - Water closet seat

1 - Toilet paper dispenser

BATHROOM CABINET
1 - 48 inch (1219 mm)
   Cabinet

1 - Countertop

1 - Self-rimming sink

1 - Bathroom sink faucet
   (not shown)

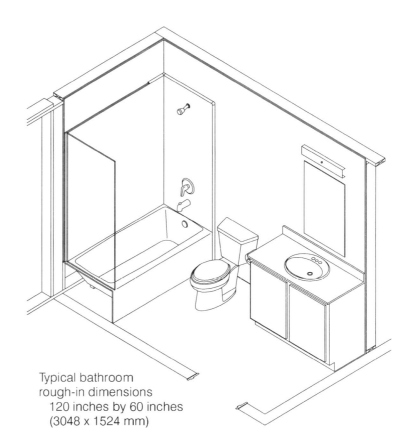

Typical bathroom
rough-in dimensions
   120 inches by 60 inches
   (3048 x 1524 mm)

Access Problems (continued)

A water closet next to a bathtub presents access problems.

- Getting into the bathtub is difficult.
- Reaching bathtub controls from a wheelchair is difficult.

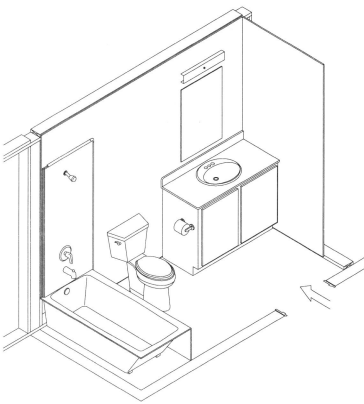

By adding grab bars and moving the vanity
and two walls:

- Getting into the bathtub is difficult.
- Reaching bathtub controls from a wheelchair
  is difficult.
- Transferring from a wheelchair to a water
  closet relies exclusively on the rear wall
  grab bar.

Regardless of the approach direction, anyone
in a wheelchair must be aware of how many
difficulties are created when a water closet
is next to a bathtub.

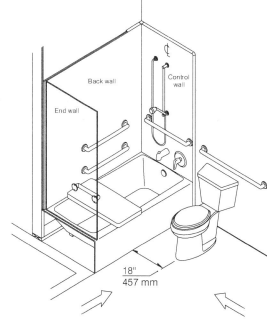

BATHROOM ONE

Although Bathroom One is the same size as the typical bathroom, there are three significant differences.

- First, the 3068 door below has approximately 33-1/2 inches (851 mm) between door and doorstop when the door is open 90 degrees.

- Second, the water closet is centered 18 inches (457 mm) away from an adjacent wall.

- Third, cabinet, countertop and sink are replaced by a lavatory.

These three differences leave enough room between a bathtub and a water closet for a Circular turning space.

BATHROOM ONE'S
ADA COMPLIANT FIXTURES

TURNING SPACE
   60 inch in diameter (1524 mm)
   Circular turning space

BATHTUB
1 - 32 inch by 60 inch
   (813 x 1524 mm)
   Bathtub

1 - Removable bathtub seat

1 - 12 inch (305 mm)
   End wall grab bar

2 - 24 inch (610 mm)
   Back wall grab bars

1 - 24 inch (610 mm)
   Control wall grab bar

1 - Bathtub/shower controls

1 - Bathtub water spout

1 - Shower spray unit

LAVATORY
1 - 22 inch by 18 inch
   (559 x 457 mm)
   Lavatory

1 - Lavatory faucet
   (not shown)

WATER CLOSET
1 - Water closet

1 - Water closet seat

1 - 36 inch (914 mm)
   Rear wall grab bar

1 - 42 inch (1067 mm)
   Side wall grab bar

1 - Toilet paper dispenser

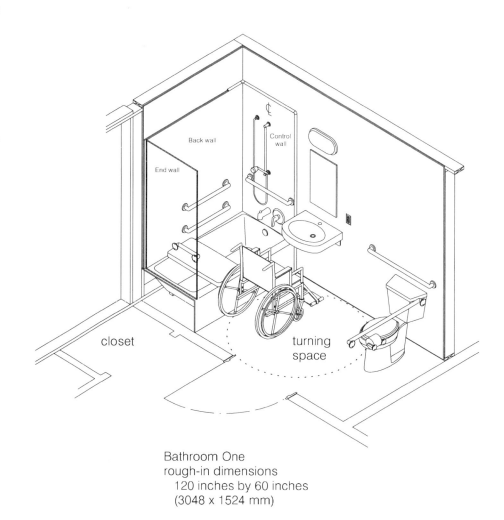

closet

turning space

Bathroom One
rough-in dimensions
120 inches by 60 inches
(3048 x 1524 mm)

Bathroom One's clear floor spaces, in concert with a turning space, allow access to each fixture.

The spaces illustrated below are:
1. Circular turning space, page 36.
2. Lavatory clear floor space, page 130.
3. Water closet clear floor space, page 118.
4. Bathtub clear floor space, page 160.
5. Front approach - push side landing, page 90.

In such a small bathroom, consider replacing a bathtub with a roll-in shower.

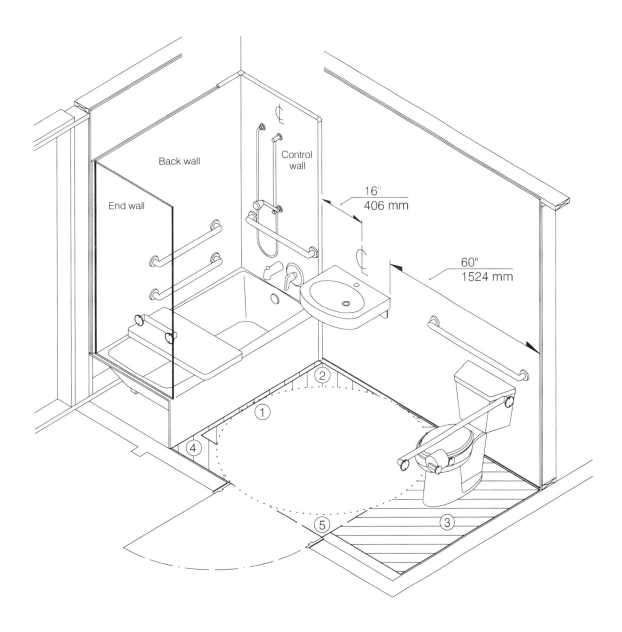

BATHROOM TWO
Roll-in Shower without Seat, Lavatory, and Water Closet

Bathroom Two's bathing fixture is a roll-in shower. A roll-in shower has a minimum width and a minimum depth, and minimum widths and depths are always considerations.

Although 30 inches (762 mm) is a roll-in shower's minimum width, a wider shower is a more comfortable space to bathe in.

A roll-in shower's 60 inch (1524 mm) minimum depth is another consideration. Note that this shower's minimum depth and the layers of building materials on both end walls make Bathroom Two 3 inches (76.2 mm) deeper than Bathroom One. A picture illustrating building materials and shower depth is on page 111.

BATHROOM TWO'S
ADA COMPLIANT FIXTURES

TURNING SPACE
    60 inch in diameter (1524 mm)
    Circular turning space

ROLL-IN SHOWER
1 - 30 inch by 60 inch
    (762 x 1524 mm)
    Roll-in shower

2 - 24 inch (610 mm)
    End wall grab bars

1 - 48 inch (1219 mm)
    Back wall grab bar

1 - Shower controls

1 - Shower spray unit

LAVATORY
1 - 22 inch by 18 inch
    (559 x 457 mm)
    Lavatory

1 - Lavatory faucet
    (not shown)

WATER CLOSET
1 - Water closet

1 - Water closet seat

1 - 36 inch (914 mm)
    Rear wall grab bar

1 - 42 inch (1067 mm)
    Side wall grab bar

1 - Toilet paper dispenser

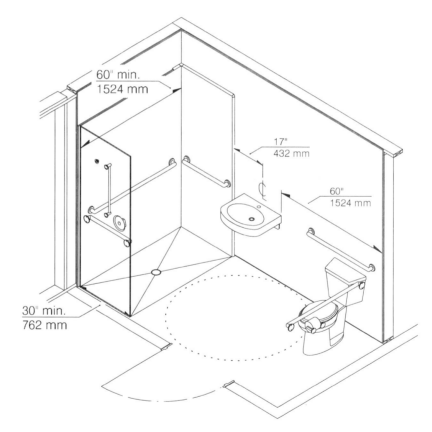

Bathroom Two
rough-in dimensions
    120 inches by 63 inches
    (3048 x 1600 mm)

BATHROOM TWO
Rough-in Dimension

A rough-in dimension is the accumulation of every item between two structural walls. This accounting for building materials and space is critical when a fixture has a minimum width or depth.

A roll-in shower with a three-ply shower surround is an example. The rough-in dimension between end walls is determined by:
- The width of the building materials on both end walls, approximately 3 inches (76.2 mm).
- The 3 inch dimension is approximate and should be accurate to within 1/4 inch (6.35 mm) given standard tiles.
- The depth of a roll-in shower.

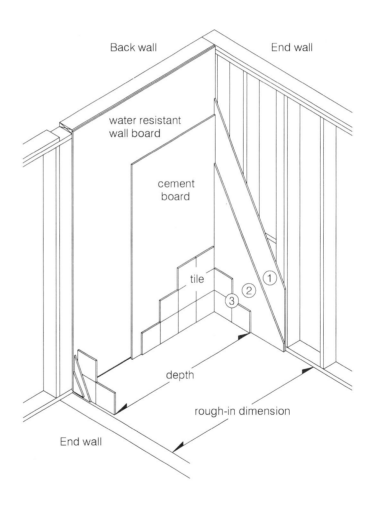

A typical shower surround has three plies.
  1st ply: 1/2 inch (12.7 mm) of water resistant wall board.
  2nd ply: 1/2 inch (12.7 mm) of cement board.
  3rd ply: 1/2 inch (12.7 mm) allowance for mastic and tile.

BATHROOM THREE
Roll-in Shower with Seat, Lavatory, and Water Closet

Bathroom Three's roll-in shower has a seat.

This roll-in shower also has a 36 inch (914 mm) wide seat wall, a seat wall wide enough for a transfer shower size L - shaped folding seat.

Bathroom Three also has additional maneuvering space beyond the seat wall.

The result is, this bathroom is 6 inches (152 mm) wider and 12 inches (305 mm) deeper than Bathroom Two.

BATHROOM THREE'S
ADA COMPLIANT FIXTURES

TURNING SPACE
  60 inch in diameter (1524 mm)
  Circular turning space

ROLL-IN SHOWER WITH SEAT
1 - 36 inch by 60 inch
  (914 x 1524 mm)
  Roll-in shower

1 - Transfer shower size
  L - shaped folding seat

1 - Shower controls

1 - Shower spray unit

1 - 36 inch (914 mm)
  Control wall grab bar

1 - 30 inch (762 mm)
  End wall grab bar

LAVATORY
1 - 22 inch by 18 inch
  (559 x 457 mm)
  Lavatory

1 - Lavatory faucet
  (not shown)

WATER CLOSET
1 - Water closet

1 - Water closet seat

1 - 36 inch (914 mm)
  Rear wall grab bar

1 - 42 inch (1067 mm)
  Side wall grab bar

1 - Toilet paper dispenser

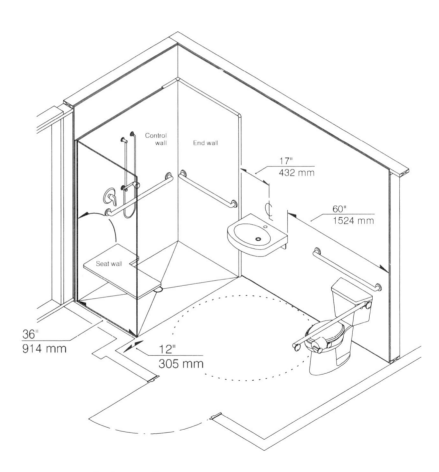

Bathroom Three
rough-in dimensions
  126 inches by 75 inches
  (3200 x 1905 mm)

BATHROOM THREE
General Rule

As a general rule, minimum widths and depth should be increased in size wherever space permits.

The length of a bathtub with a permanent seat's clear floor space is the depth of the bathtub and seat and 12 inches (305 mm) beyond the seat wall. Width and depth details are on page 168.

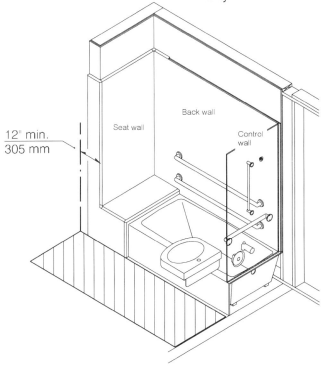

12" min.
305 mm

Seat wall

Back wall

Control wall

An example of an increase in space is an additional 12 inches (305 mm) in depth beyond a roll-in shower's seat wall. This extra space makes maneuvering in and out of a shower easier.

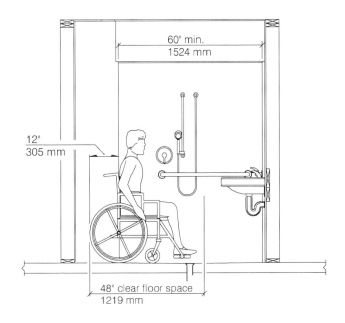

60" min.
1524 mm

12"
305 mm

48" clear floor space
1219 mm

BATHROOM FOUR
Alternate Shower with Seat, Lavatory, and Water Closet

Combining some of the design characteristics of a transfer shower, page 190, and an alternate shower with seat, page 196, creates a bathing fixture with advantages.

- There is a grab bar forward of the approach to aid the transfer from wheelchair to seat.
- The seat wall is wide enough for an L - shaped folding seat.
- The folding seat, in an up position, gives the shower dual use.
- The controls and shower spray unit are opposite the seat.
- The showerhead, it its fixed position and when it is handheld, can have its spray directed away from the entrance.

BATHROOM FOUR'S
ADA COMPLIANT FIXTURES

TURNING SPACE
    60 inch in diameter (1524 mm)
    Circular turning space

ALTERNATE SHOWER
1 - 72 inch by 36 inch
    (1829 x 914 mm)
    Alternate shower with seat
    and back wall controls

1 - Shower controls

1 - Shower spray unit

1 - 60 inch (1524 mm)
    Back wall grab bar

1 - 12 inch (305 mm)
    End wall grab bar

1 - Transfer shower size
    L - shaped folding seat

LAVATORY
1 - 22 inch by 18 inch
    (559 x 457 mm)
    Lavatory

1 - Lavatory faucet
    (not shown)

WATER CLOSET
1 - Water closet

1 - Water closet seat

1 - 36 inch (914 mm)
    Rear wall grab bar

1 - 42 inch (1067 mm)
    Side wall grab bar

1 - Toilet paper dispenser

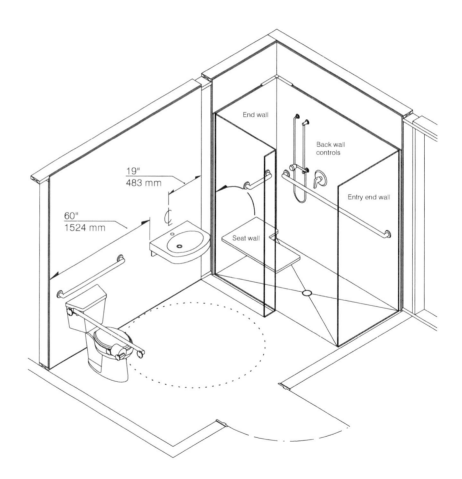

Bathroom Four
rough-in dimensions
    136 inches by 75 inches
    (3454 x 1905 mm)

BATHROOM NOTES

Making sure a person can enter a bathroom, use any fixture in any order, turn around and leave requires planning. It also requires answers to basic questions.

- Is a fixture readily available?

- Which approach clear floor space makes a fixture accessible?

- Does a fixture require knee clearance?

- Where are a fixture's hard edges?

- How does a turning space lead from one fixture to the other fixtures in the bathroom?

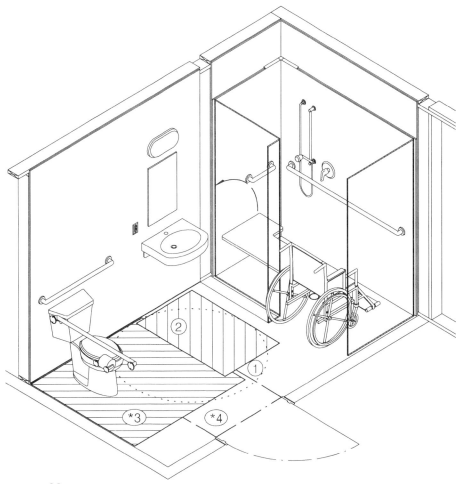

Overlapping Spaces
1. Circular turning space, page 36.
2. Lavatory clear floor space, page 130.
3. Water closet clear floor space, page 118.*
4. Front approach - push side landing, page 90.*

(* partially covered)

NOTES

WATER CLOSET

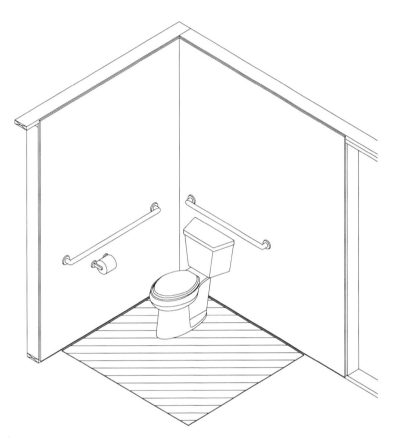

WATER CLOSET
Design Considerations

One difference between a water closet in public spaces and a water closet in a single-family home is the height of the seat.

Public spaces have the top of a water closet's seat at 17 to 19 inches (432 - 483 mm) above the finished floor, which is closer to the height of a typical wheelchair seat. Residential guidelines have the top of the seat at 15 to 19 inches (381 - 483 mm) above the finished floor.

A caution about installing a water closet next to a bathtub is on page 107. Also, when a lavatory is installed the minimum distance away from a water closet, the water closet has a larger clear floor space than the one pictured below. An illustration is on page 122.

■ Other views of a water closet and fixtures are on page 126 and page 127.

WATER CLOSET'S
ADA COMPLIANT FIXTURES

CLEAR FLOOR SPACE
  56 inch by 60 inch
  (1422 x 1524 mm)
  Water closet
  clear floor space

WATER CLOSET
1 - Water closet

1 - Water closet seat

1 - 36 inch (914 mm)
  Rear wall grab bar

1 - 42 inch (1067 mm)
  Side wall grab bar

1 - Toilet paper dispenser

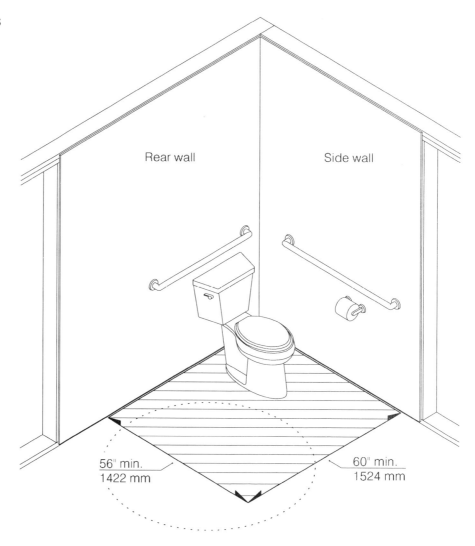

Rear wall

Side wall

56" min.
1422 mm

60" min.
1524 mm

WATER CLOSET
Typical Guidelines

SIDE WALL

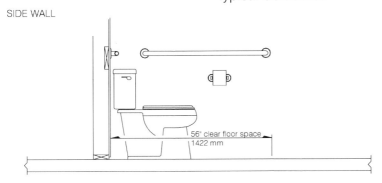

56" clear floor space
1422 mm

WATER CLOSET
CLEAR FLOOR SPACE
a. 56 inches (1422 mm) minimum
from the rear wall.
b. 60 inches (1524 mm) minimum
from the side wall.

REAR WALL

16" min. - 18" max
406 - 457 mm

15" min. - 19" max
381 - 483 mm

WATER CLOSET SEAT HEIGHT
15 inches (381 mm) minimum and
19 inches (483 mm) maximum
from the top of the seat to the
finished floor.

WATER CLOSET CENTERLINE
16 inches (406 mm) minimum and
18 inches (457 mm) maximum
from the side wall to the centerline.

FIXTURE NEXT TO A WATER CLOSET
Illustrations are on pages 122 and 123.

REAR WALL

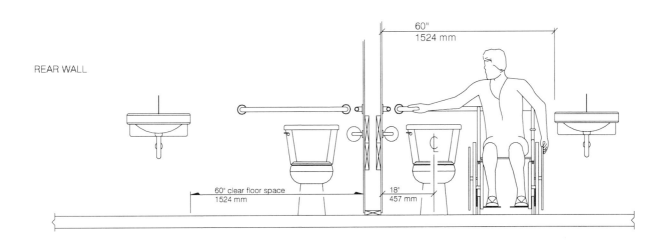

60"
1524 mm

60" clear floor space
1524 mm

18"
457 mm

WATER CLOSET   119

WATER CLOSET
Typical Guidelines

SIDE WALL

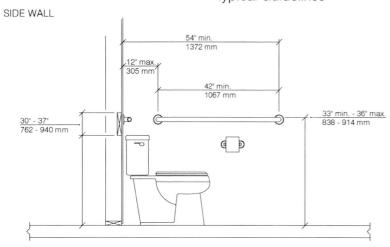

GRAB BAR HEIGHT (typical)
a.   Installed a uniform horizontal height
     above the finished floor.
b.   33 inches (838 mm) minimum and
     36 inches (914 mm) maximum
     from the top of the gripping surface
     to the finished floor.

SIDE WALL GRAB BAR
a.   Typical height.
b.   12 inches (305 mm) maximum
     from the rear wall.
c.   42 inches (1067 mm) minimum
     in length.
d.   54 inches (1372 mm) minimum
     from the rear wall.

REAR WALL

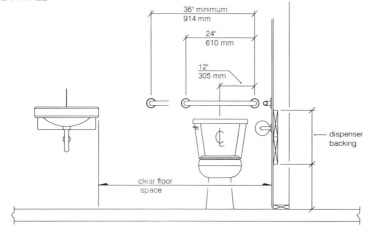

REAR WALL GRAB BAR
a.   Typical height.
b.   36 inches (914 mm) minimum in length,
     with 24 inches (610 mm) on the transfer
     side of the water closet's centerline.
c.   24 inches minimum in length, centered
     on the water closet, when the location
     of an adjacent fixture does not permit
     a 36 inch grab bar.

     ■ A water closet with a 24 inch rear wall
       grab bar is illustrated on page 122.

GRAB BAR BACKING (typical)
   30 inches to 37 inches (762 - 940 mm)
   above the finished floor.

SIDE WALL

PAPER DISPENSER
LOCATION
a.   1-1/2 inches (38.1 mm) minimum
     between the dispenser and the
     bottom of the side wall grab bar.
b.   15 inches (381 mm) minimum
     above the finished floor.
c.   Centered
        7 inches (178 mm) minimum and
        9 inches (229 mm) maximum
        from the water closet's front edge.

WATER CLOSET
Rough-in Considerations

A bathroom plan should detail:
- Net thickness of each structural wall and wall covering.
- Drain location.
- Clear floor space.
- Finished floor height.
- Grab bar and dispenser backing locations.
- Turning space to and away from a water closet.
- Location of nearby fixtures.

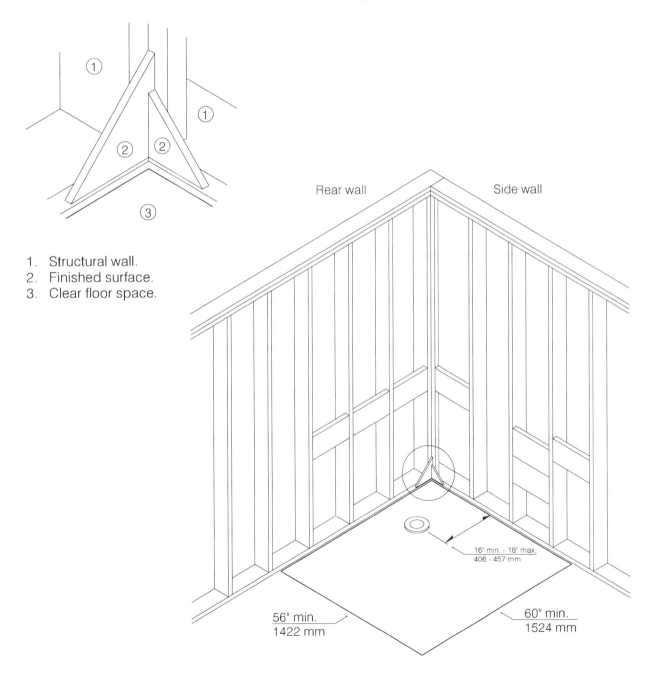

1. Structural wall.
2. Finished surface.
3. Clear floor space.

Rear wall

Side wall

16" min. - 18" max.
406 - 457 mm

56" min.
1422 mm

60" min.
1524 mm

LAVATORY NEXT TO A WATER CLOSET
Minimum Distance

Although a locality may permit a lavatory's edge 18 inches
(457 mm) minimum from the centerline of a water closet when
a water closet has the larger clear floor space detailed below,
the general rule is, minimum widths and depths should be
increased in size wherever space permits. This includes
the space between a lavatory and a water closet.

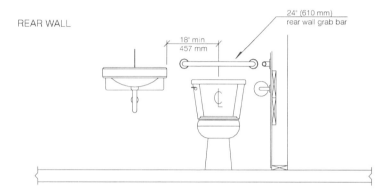

REAR WALL

24" (610 mm)
rear wall grab bar

18" min
457 mm

WATER CLOSET
CLEAR FLOOR SPACE
   66 inches (1676 mm) minimum
   from the rear wall and
   60 inches (1524 mm) minimum
   from the side wall when a lavatory
   is 18 inches minimum from the
   water closet's centerline.

LAVATORY NEXT TO A WATER CLOSET
   18 inches (457 mm) minimum
   from the centerline of a water closet
   when the water closet has the 66" x 60"
   clear floor space detailed above.

GRAB BAR HEIGHT (typical)
   a. Installed a uniform horizontal height
      above the finished floor.
   b. 33 inches (838 mm) minimum and
      36 inches (914 mm) maximum
      from the top of the gripping surface
      to the finished floor.

GRAB BAR BACKING (typical)
   30 inches to 37 inches (762 - 940 mm)
   above the finished floor.

REAR WALL GRAB BAR
   a. Typical height.
   b. 36 inches (914 mm) minimum in length,
      with 24 inches (610 mm) on the transfer
      side of the water closet's centerline.
   c. 24 inches minimum in length, centered
      on the water closet, when the location
      of an adjacent fixture does not permit
      a 36 inch grab bar.

     ■ A water closet with a 36 inch
       rear wall grab bar is illustrated
       on page 123.

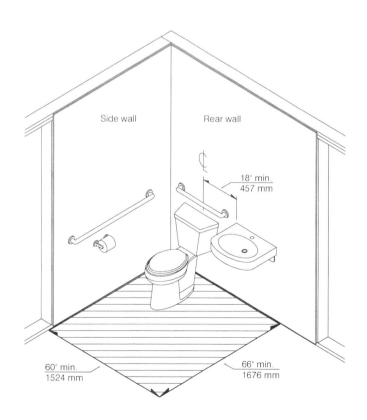

Side wall

Rear wall

18" min.
457 mm

60" min.
1524 mm

66" min.
1676 mm

FIXTURE NEXT TO A WATER CLOSET

With a water closet adjacent to the side wall, 60 inches (1524 mm) between the side wall and a fixture has advantages.

- There is room to install a 36 inch (914 mm) rear wall grab bar.
- Maneuvering near a water closet is easier.

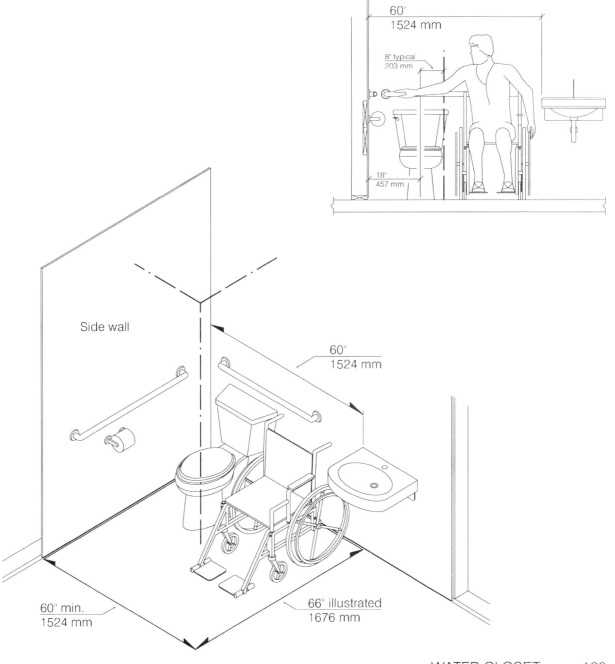

60"
1524 mm

8" typical
203 mm

18"
457 mm

Side wall

60"
1524 mm

60" min.
1524 mm

66" illustrated
1676 mm

WATER CLOSET HARD EDGES
Front Edge

30 inches (762 mm) is the typical distance from the rear wall to the front edge of a water closet.

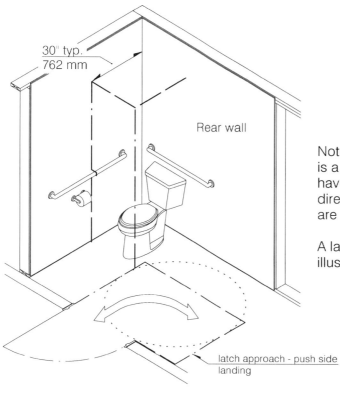

30" typ.
762 mm

Rear wall

latch approach - push side landing

Note: A landing on each side of a doorway is a constant. A landing's width and depth have several determining factors. Approach direction, hardware location, and door swing are only three of the considerations.

A latch approach - push side landing is illustrated.

Having 66 inches (1676 mm) of clearance from the rear wall makes maneuvering near a water closet easier.

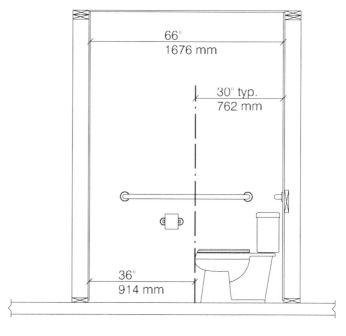

66"
1676 mm

30" typ.
762 mm

36"
914 mm

WATER CLOSET HARD EDGES
Seat Side Edge

26 inches (660 mm) is the typical distance from the side wall to the seat side edge when a water closet's centerline is 18 inches (457 mm) from the side wall.

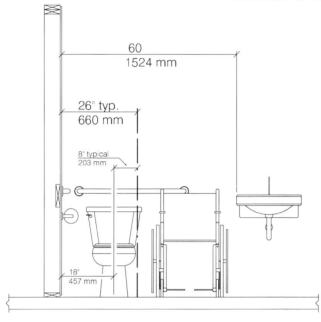

60
1524 mm

26" typ.
660 mm

8" typical
203 mm

18"
457 mm

Having a 66 by 60 inch (1524 x 1676 mm) clear floor space makes maneuvering near a water closet easier.

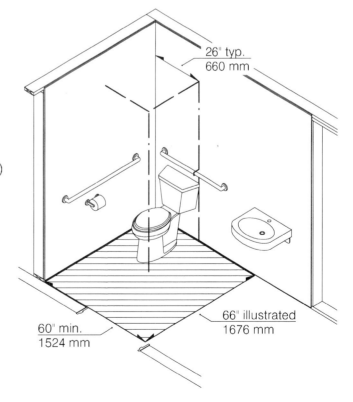

26" typ.
660 mm

60" min.
1524 mm

66" illustrated
1676 mm

OVERLAPPING SPACES

Turning space and clear floor space can overlap.

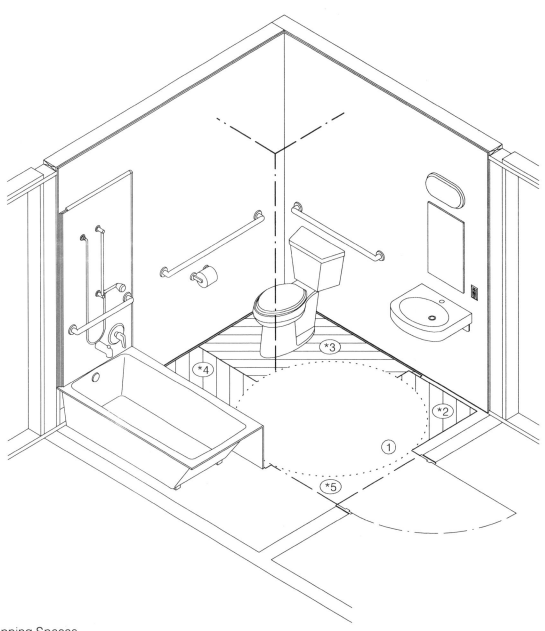

Overlapping Spaces
1. Circular turning space, page 36.
2. Lavatory clear floor space, page 130.*
3. Water closet clear floor space, page 118.*
4. Bathtub clear floor space, page 160.*
5. Front approach - push side landing, page 90.*

(* partially covered)

Wheelchair accessibility is the ability to enter a home, use any fixture in any order, turn around and leave.

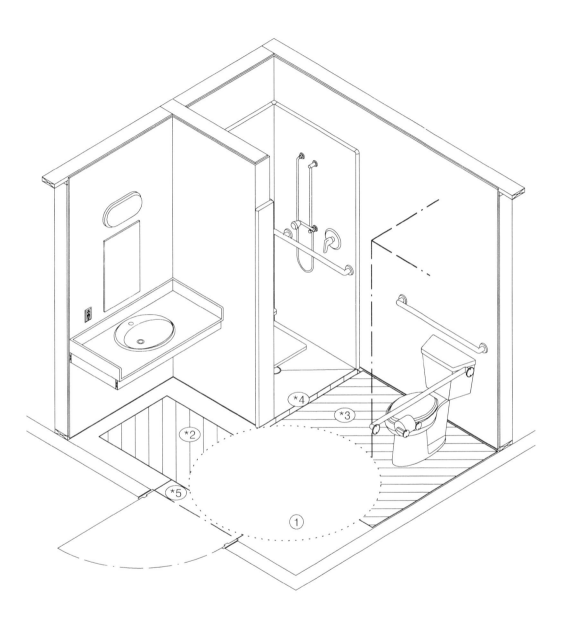

Overlapping Spaces
  1. Circular turning space, page 36.
  2. Sink clear floor space, page 144.*
  3. Water closet clear floor space, page 118.*
  4. Transfer shower clear floor space, page 190.*
  5. Front approach - push side landing, page 90.*

      (* partially covered)

NOTES

LAVATORY

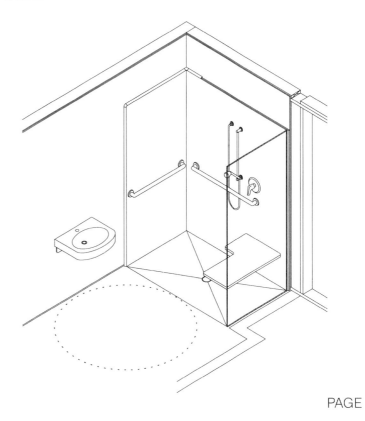

LAVATORY
Design Considerations

A lavatory's forward approach clear floor space, 30 inches in width by 48 inches in depth (762 x 1219 mm), is centered on the lavatory.

The approach clear floor space, in concert with knee clearance, allows a person to keep both hands forward while the lavatory is being used.

A turning space under a lavatory also has an advantage. It provides maneuvering space near an adjacent fixture that a cabinet, countertop and sink cannot provide.

Knee clearance beneath a lavatory is illustrated on page 132.

LAVATORY'S
ADA COMPLIANT FIXTURES

CLEAR FLOOR SPACE
    30 inch by 48 inch
    (762 x 1219 mm)
    Lavatory
    forward approach
    clear floor space

KNEE AND TOE SPACE

LAVATORY
1 - 22 inch by 18 inch
    (559 x 457 mm)
    Lavatory
    + ADA wrap

1 - Lavatory faucet
    (not shown)

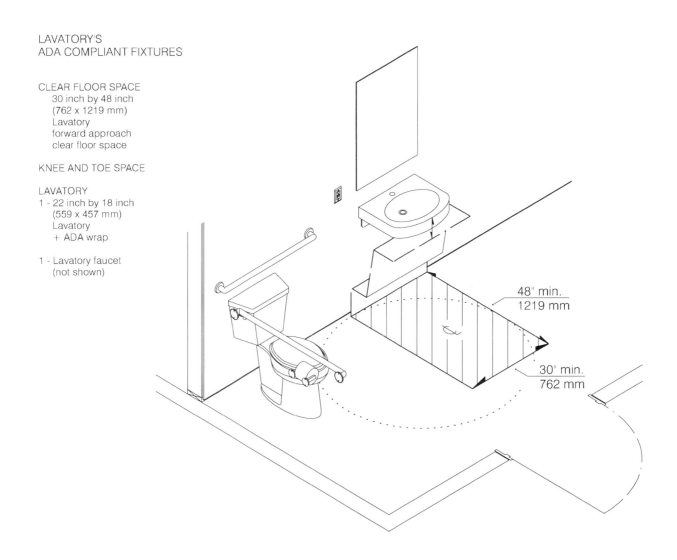

48" min.
1219 mm

30" min.
762 mm

LAVATORY
Typical Guidelines

REAR WALL

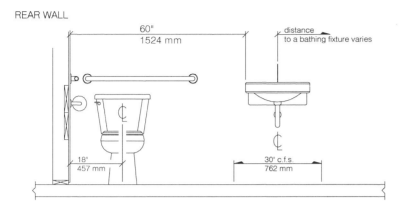

SIDE VIEW

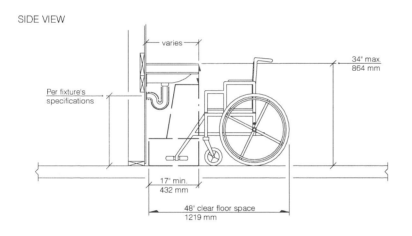

SIDE VIEW

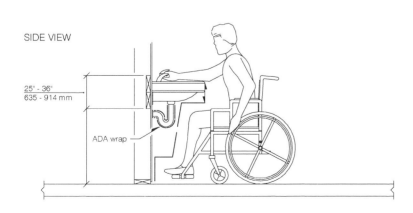

LAVATORY
FORWARD APPROACH
CLEAR FLOOR SPACE
  a. 30 inches (762 mm) minimum
      in width centered on the sink.
  b. 48 inches (1219 mm) minimum
      in depth.

LAVATORY HEIGHT
  34 inches (864 mm) maximum
  above the finished floor.

FIXTURE NEXT TO A WATER CLOSET
  Illustrations are on pages 134 and 135.

DISTANCE FROM THE CENTERLINE OF
A LAVATORY TO A BATHING FIXTURE
  Basic relationships between a lavatory
  and bathing fixtures are on pages
  136 - 140.

KNEE AND TOE SPACE
  Knee and toe space guidelines are on
  page 132.

DRAIN LOCATION
  Per fixture's specifications.

ADA WRAP
  The padding around a drain assembly.

LAVATORY HANGER BACKING
  Per fixture's specifications.

- Solid blocking 25 inches to 36 inches
  (635 - 914 mm) above the finished floor
  is illustrated.

KNEE AND TOE SPACE
Typical Guidelines

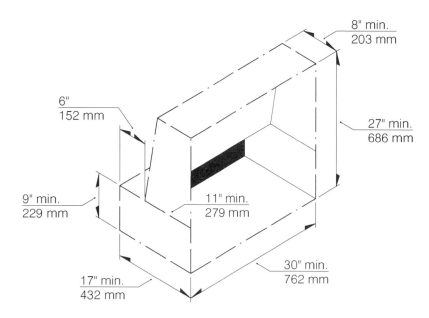

8" min.
203 mm

6"
152 mm

27" min.
686 mm

9" min.
229 mm

11" min.
279 mm

30" min.
762 mm

17" min.
432 mm

KNEE SPACE
a. 30 inches (762 mm) minimum
in width.
b. 8 inches (203 mm) minimum
in depth at 27 inches (686 mm)
above the finished floor.
c. 11 inches (279 mm) minimum
in depth at 9 inches (229 mm)
above the finished floor.
d. Between 9 and 27 inches above
the finished floor knee space is
permitted to reduce at a rate of
1 inch in depth for every six inches
in height.

TOE SPACE
a. 30 inches (762 mm) minimum
in width.
b. 17 inches (432 mm) minimum
in depth.
c. 25 inches (635 mm) maximum
in depth.
d. 9 inches (229 mm) minimum
above the finished floor.
e. At 9 inches above the finished floor,
space more than 6 inches (152 mm)
beyond the knee clearance is not
considered toe space.

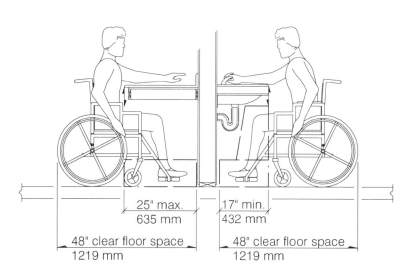

25" max.
635 mm

17" min.
432 mm

48" clear floor space
1219 mm

48" clear floor space
1219 mm

Note: Clearance above, below, behind, and at both sides
of a fixture are critical.

Typically, ADA compliant fixtures that require knee clearance
have a specifications sheet that details:
- Knee and toe space.
- Fixture height above the finished floor.
- Fixture distance from the front of a countertop.
- Side wall, back wall, and cabinet structure's minimum
clearance around heated elements, electrical hookups,
gas hookups, drain assembly, supply lines, and the like.

LAVATORY IN AN ALCOVE

Forward Approach
An alcove, with a forward approach, that is more than 24 inches (610 mm) deep is 36 inches (914 mm) minimum in width.

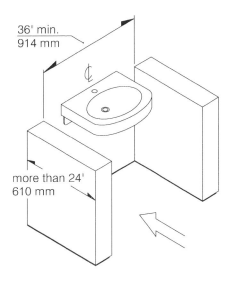

36" min.
914 mm

more than 24"
610 mm

Parallel Approach
An alcove, with a parallel approach, that is more than 15 inches (381 mm) wide is 60 inches (1524 mm) minimum in depth.

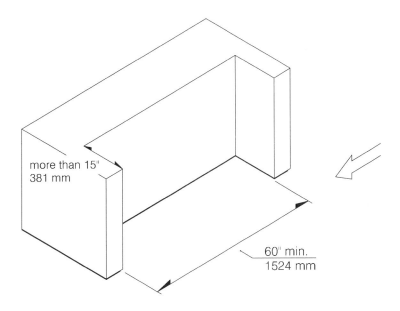

more than 15"
381 mm

60" min.
1524 mm

LAVATORY NEXT TO A WATER CLOSET
Minimum Distance

Although a locality may permit a lavatory's edge 18 inches (457 mm) minimum from the centerline of a water closet when a water closet has the larger clear floor space detailed below, the general rule is, minimum widths and depths should be increased in size wherever space permits. This includes the space between a lavatory and a water closet.

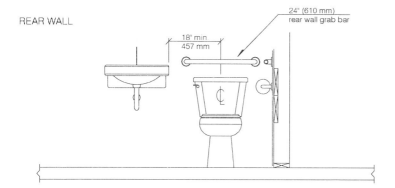

REAR WALL

WATER CLOSET
CLEAR FLOOR SPACE
  66 inches (1676 mm) minimum
  from the rear wall and
  60 inches (1524 mm) minimum
  from the side wall when a lavatory
  is 18 inches minimum from the
  water closet's centerline.

LAVATORY NEXT TO A WATER CLOSET
  18 inches (457 mm) minimum
  from the centerline of a water closet
  when the water closet has the 66" x 60"
  clear floor space detailed above.

GRAB BAR HEIGHT (typical)
  a. Installed a uniform horizontal height
      above the finished floor.
  b. 33 inches (838 mm) minimum and
      36 inches (914 mm) maximum
      from the top of the gripping surface
      to the finished floor.

GRAB BAR BACKING (typical)
  30 inches to 37 inches (762 - 940 mm)
  above the finished floor.

REAR WALL GRAB BAR
  a. Typical height.
  b. 36 inches (914 mm) minimum in length,
      with 24 inches (610 mm) on the transfer
      side of the water closet's centerline.
  c. 24 inches minimum in length, centered
      on the water closet, when the location
      of an adjacent fixture does not permit
      a 36 inch grab bar.

  ■ A water closet with a 36 inch
     rear wall grab bar is illustrated
     on page 135.

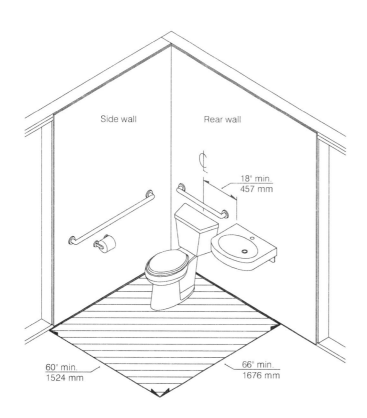

FIXTURE NEXT TO A WATER CLOSET

With a water closet adjacent to the side wall, 60 inches (1524 mm) between the side wall and a fixture has advantages.

- There is room to install a 36 inch (914 mm) rear wall grab bar.
- Maneuvering near a water closet is easier.

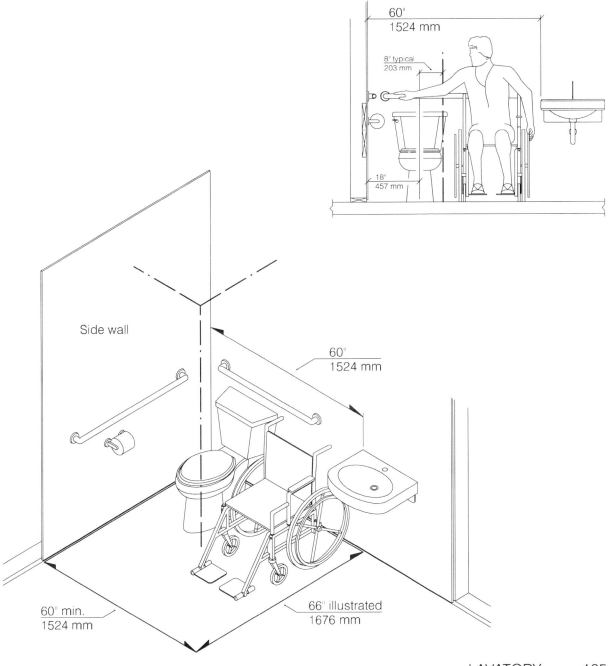

60"
1524 mm

8" typical
203 mm

18"
457 mm

Side wall

60"
1524 mm

60" min.
1524 mm

66" illustrated
1676 mm

LAVATORY NEXT TO A BATHING FIXTURE
Bathtub

A bathtub's clear floor space is 30 inches (762 mm) minimum in width. A lavatory is permitted on the 30 inch end adjacent to a bathtub's control wall.

BATHTUB
CLEAR FLOOR SPACE
a. 30 inches (762 mm) minimum in width.
b. The depth of the bathtub.

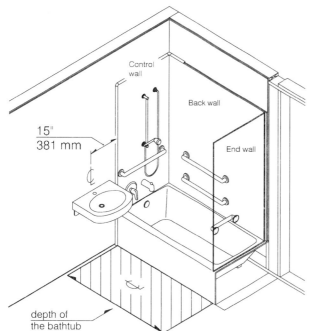

Lavatory Position
- Installed on the wall adjacent to a bathtub's control wall.
- Centered on a bathtub's clear floor space.

CIRCULAR TURNING SPACE
60 inches (1524 mm) is the minimum diameter of a Circular turning space.

Lavatory Position
- Centered on a Circular turning space.

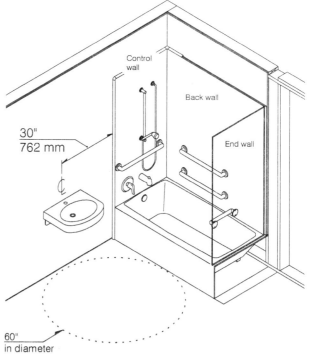

LAVATORY NEXT TO A BATHING FIXTURE
Roll-in Shower without Seat

A roll-in shower's clear floor space is 30 inches (762 mm) minimum in width. A lavatory is permitted on the 30 inch end opposite a roll-in shower without seat's end wall controls.

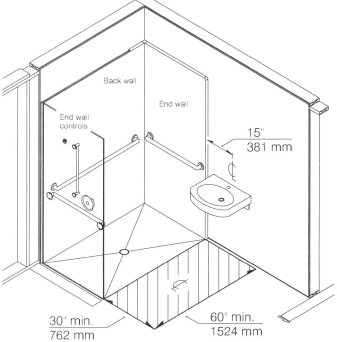

ROLL-IN SHOWER
CLEAR FLOOR SPACE
30 inches (762 mm) minimum in width by
60 inches (1524 mm) minimum in depth
adjacent to the shower's open side.

Back wall

End wall

End wall controls

15"
381 mm

30" min.
762 mm

60" min.
1524 mm

Lavatory Position
- Installed opposite a roll-in shower without seat's end wall controls.
- Centered on a roll-in shower's clear floor space.

As a general rule, minimum widths and depths should be increased in size wherever space permits.

Lavatory Position
- Installed opposite a roll-in shower without seat's end wall, the end wall closest to the back wall controls.
- Centered on a Circular turning space.

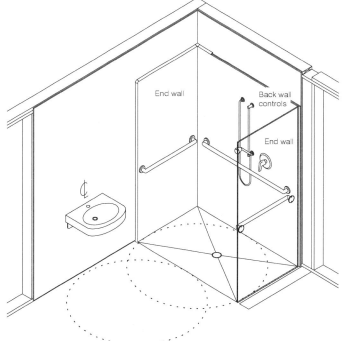

End wall

Back wall controls

End wall

LAVATORY NEXT TO A BATHING FIXTURE
Bathing Fixture with Seat

Both a bathtub with permanent seat and a roll-in shower with seat have, at minimum, a 30 inch (762 mm) wide clear floor space. A lavatory is permitted on the 30 inch end opposite a roll-in shower's seat and the 30 inch end opposite a bathtub's permanent seat.

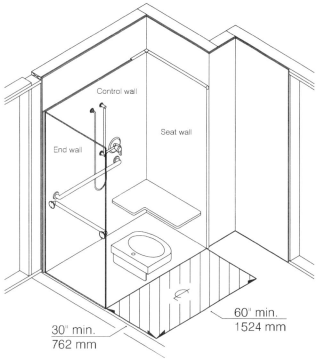

Control wall

Seat wall

End wall

30" min.
762 mm

60" min.
1524 mm

ROLL-IN SHOWER
CLEAR FLOOR SPACE
  30 inches (762 mm) minimum in width by
  60 inches (1524 mm) minimum in depth
  adjacent to the shower's open side.

Lavatory Position
- Installed on the wall opposite a roll-in shower's seat.
- Centered on a roll-in shower's clear floor space.

BATHTUB WITH PERMANENT SEAT
CLEAR FLOOR SPACE
  a. 30 inches (762 mm) minimum in width.
  b. Depth of bathtub and seat and 12 inches (305 mm) beyond the seat wall.

Lavatory Position
- Installed on the wall opposite a bathtub's permanent seat.
- Centered on a bathtub with permanent seat's clear floor space.

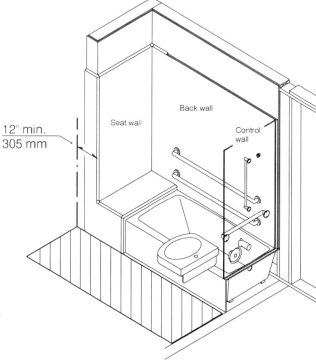

12" min.
305 mm

Seat wall

Back wall

Control wall

LAVATORY NEXT TO A BATHING FIXTURE
Transfer Shower

A lavatory should neither overlap a transfer shower's clear floor space nor obstruct a turn in and away from that clear floor space.

TRANSFER SHOWER
CLEAR FLOOR SPACE
36 inches (914 mm) minimum in width by 48 inches (1219 mm) minimum in depth measured from the control wall.

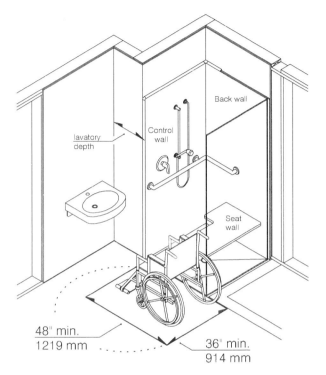

Back wall

lavatory depth

Control wall

Seat wall

48" min.
1219 mm

36" min.
914 mm

Lavatory Position
■ Beyond a transfer shower's clear floor space.

Lavatory Position
■ Beyond a transfer shower's clear floor space.

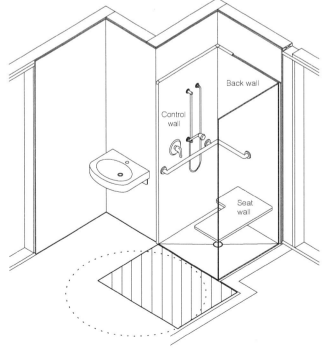

Back wall

Control wall

Seat wall

LAVATORY NEXT TO A BATHING FIXTURE
Alternate Shower with Seat

A lavatory cannot obstruct an alternate shower's entry.

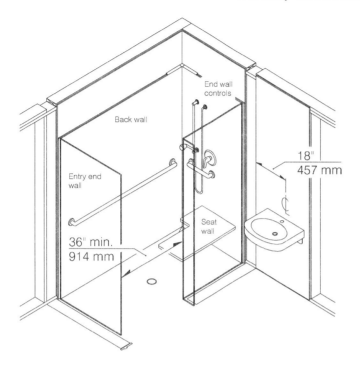

ALTERNATE SHOWER ENTRY
36 inches (914 mm) minimum
in width.

Back wall

End wall controls

Entry end wall

Seat wall

18"
457 mm

36" min.
914 mm

Lavatory Position
- Clear of an alternate shower's entry.

MANEUVERING IN AND MANEUVERING OUT

Approaching a lavatory, using it, and turning around are all part of the access equation.

Where space permits, increasing the size of a turning space makes maneuvering from fixture to fixture easier.

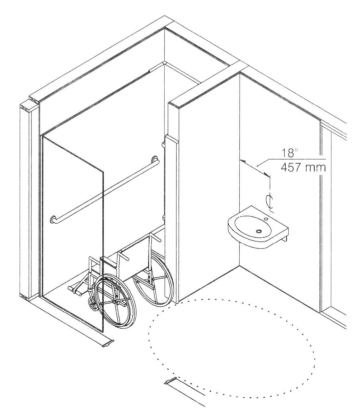

18"
457 mm

OVERLAPPING SPACES

Turning space and clear floor space can overlap.

Wheelchair accessibility is the ability to enter a home, use any fixture in any order, turn around and leave.

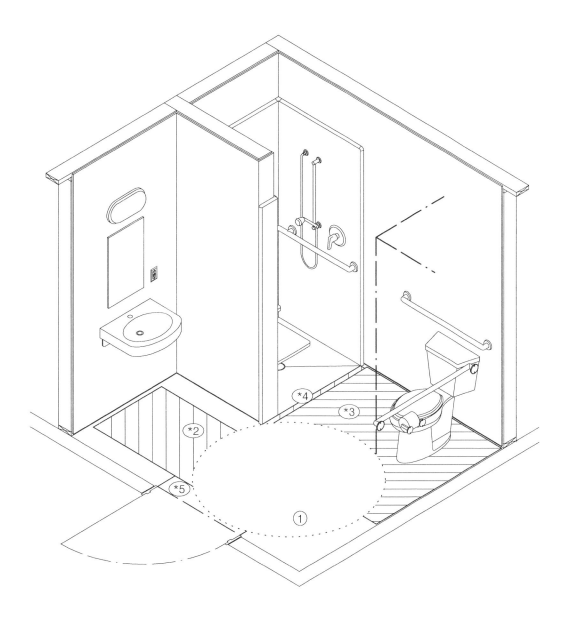

Overlapping Spaces
1. Circular turning space, page 36.
2. Lavatory clear floor space, page 130.*
3. Water closet clear floor space, page 118.*
4. Transfer shower clear floor space, page 190.*
5. Front approach - push side landing, page 90.*

(* partially covered)

NOTES

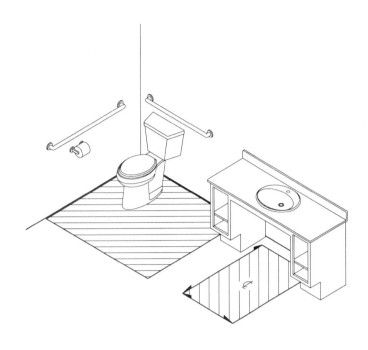

BATHROOM SINK WITH FORWARD APPROACH

An ADA compliant sink and a forward approach allows a person to keep both hands forward while using a sink.

Typically, ADA compliant fixtures that require knee clearance have a specifications sheet that details:
- Knee and toe space.
- Fixture height above the finished floor.
- Fixture distance from the front of a countertop.
- Side wall, back wall, and cabinet structure's minimum clearance around heated elements, electrical hookups, gas hookups, drain assembly, supply lines, and the like.

Knee and toe space guidelines are on page 132.

ADA COMPLIANT FIXTURES

CLEAR FLOOR SPACE
　　30 inch by 48 inch
　　(762 x 1219 mm)
　　Sink
　　forward approach
　　clear floor space

KNEE AND TOE SPACE

CABINETS, COUNTERTOP AND SINK
2 - 12 inch (305 mm) wide
　　Universal access
　　bathroom cabinets
　　with a 36 inch (914 mm)
　　space between cabinets

1 - Countertop

1 - Self-rimming sink
　　+ ADA wrap

1 - Bathroom sink faucet
　　(not shown)

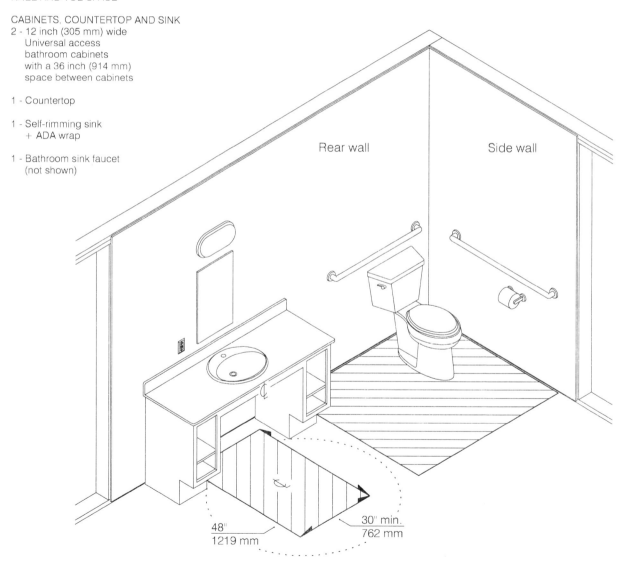

Rear wall　　　　Side wall

48"
1219 mm

30" min.
762 mm

BATHROOM SINK WITH FORWARD APPROACH
Typical Guidelines

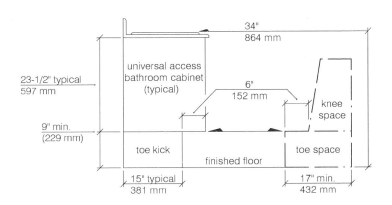

23-1/2" typical
597 mm

9" min.
(229 mm)

34"
864 mm

universal access
bathroom cabinet
(typical)

6"
152 mm

knee
space

toe kick

finished floor

toe space

15" typical
381 mm

17" min.
432 mm

REAR WALL

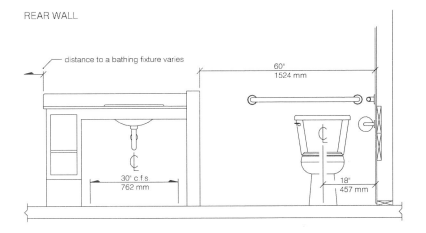

distance to a bathing fixture varies

60"
1524 mm

30" c.f.s.
762 mm

18"
457 mm

SIDE VIEW

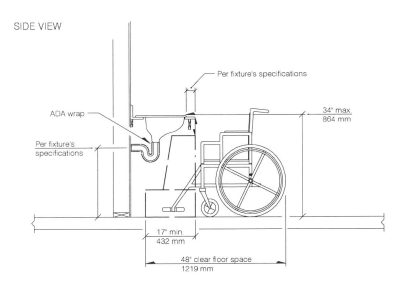

Per fixture's specifications

ADA wrap

Per fixture's
specifications

34" max.
864 mm

17" min.
432 mm

48" clear floor space
1219 mm

UNIVERSAL ACCESS BATHROOM CABINET
  a. Toe kick (cabinet base)
     1. 9 inches (229 mm) minimum
        above the finished floor.
     2. 15 inches (381 mm) in depth.
  b. Toe space
     1. 9 inches (229 mm) minimum
        above the finished floor.
     2. 6 inches (152 mm) in depth.
  c. Cabinet height
     23-1/2 inches (597 mm) typical.
  d. Cabinet depth
     21 inches (533 mm) typical.

SINK
FORWARD APPROACH
CLEAR FLOOR SPACE
  a. 30 inches (762 mm) minimum
     in width centered on the sink.
  b. 48 inches (1219 mm) minimum
     in depth.

SINK HEIGHT
  34 inches (864 mm) maximum
  above the finished floor.

SINK AND DRAIN LOCATION
  Per fixture's specifications.

ADA WRAP
  The padding around a drain assembly.

KNEE AND TOE SPACE
  Knee and toe space guidelines are on
  page 132.

FIXTURE NEXT TO A WATER CLOSET
  An illustration is on page 149.

DISTANCE TO A BATHING FIXTURE
  Basic relationships between a cabinet,
  countertop, and bathing fixtures are on
  pages 152 - 156.

BATHROOM SIZE

A t-shaped turn is pictured below.   36 inches (914 mm) between cabinets is illustrated.

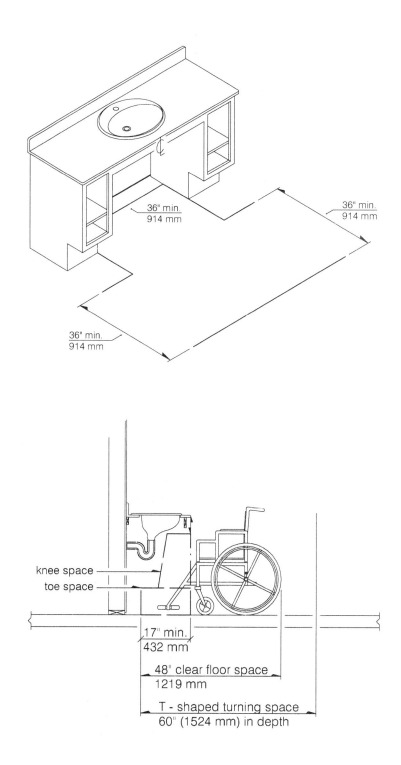

36" min.
914 mm

36" min.
914 mm

36" min.
914 mm

knee space
toe space

17" min.
432 mm

48" clear floor space
1219 mm

T - shaped turning space
60" (1524 mm) in depth

BATHROOM SIZE

Below, a Circular turning space takes advantage of an accessible toe space. 46 inches (1168 mm) between cabinets is illustrated.

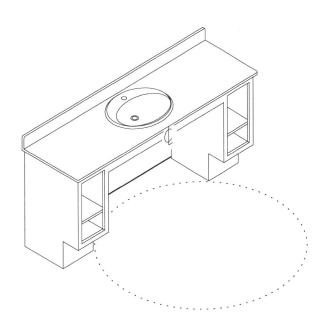

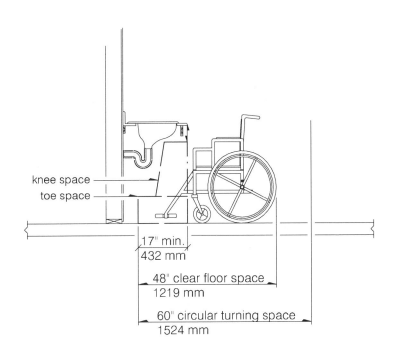

knee space
toe space

17" min.
432 mm

48" clear floor space
1219 mm

60" circular turning space
1524 mm

BATHROOM CABINET, COUNTERTOP AND SINK   147

WATER CLOSET HARD EDGES

Front Edge

30 inches (762 mm) is the typical distance from the rear wall to the front edge of a water closet.

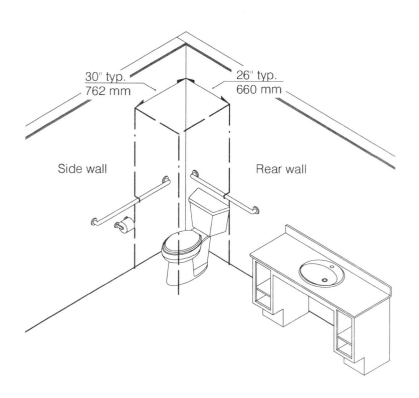

30" typ.
762 mm

26" typ.
660 mm

Side wall

Rear wall

Seat Side Edge

26 inches (660 mm) is the typical distance from the side wall to the seat side edge when a water closet's centerline is 18 inches (457 mm) from the side wall.

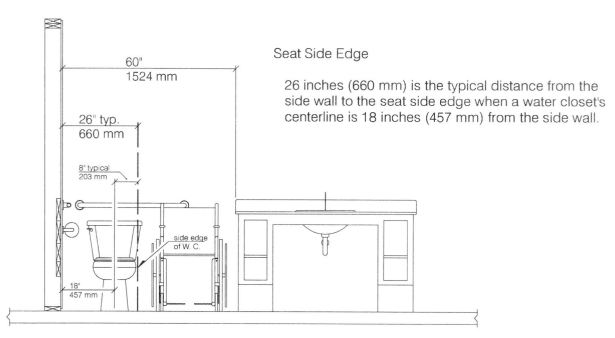

60"
1524 mm

26" typ.
660 mm

8" typical
203 mm

side edge
of W. C.

18"
457 mm

FIXTURE NEXT TO A WATER CLOSET

With a water closet adjacent to the side wall, 60 inches (1524 mm) between the side wall and a fixture has advantages.

- There is room to install a 36 inch (914 mm) rear wall grab bar.
- Maneuvering near a water closet is easier.

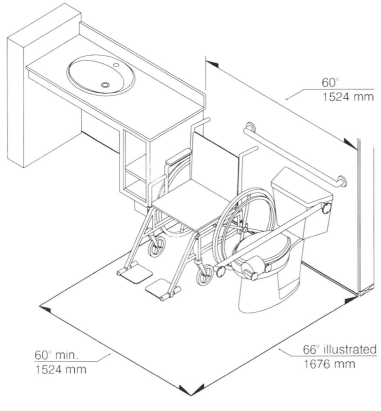

60"
1524 mm

60" min.
1524 mm

66" illustrated
1676 mm

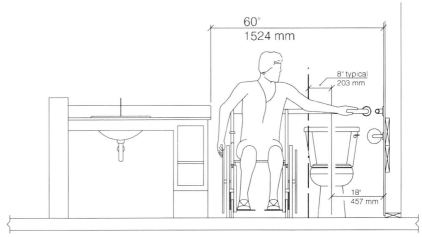

60"
1524 mm

8" typical
203 mm

18"
457 mm

CABINET, COUNTERTOP, BATHING FIXTURE,
AND TURNING SPACE

The picture below illustrates an access problem.

Given:
- The structural walls.
- The countertop 36 inches (914 mm) away from the bathtub's control wall.

Neither a Circular turning space nor a T - shaped turning space allow a 180 degree turn to and away from the bathtub's controls.

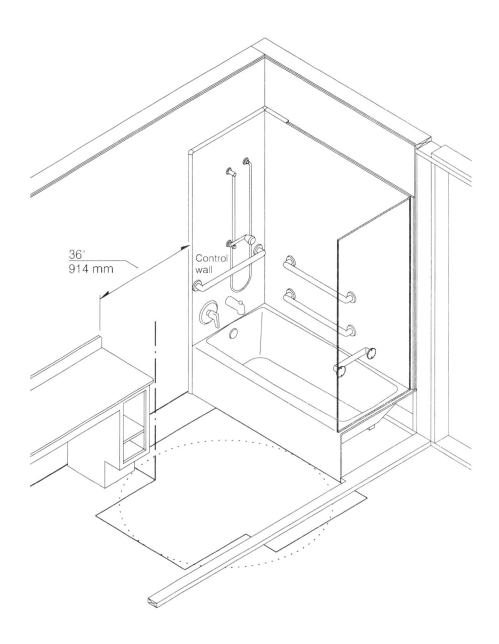

CABINET, COUNTERTOP, AND TURNING SPACE

In both pictures below, a Circular turning space takes advantage of an accessible toe space.

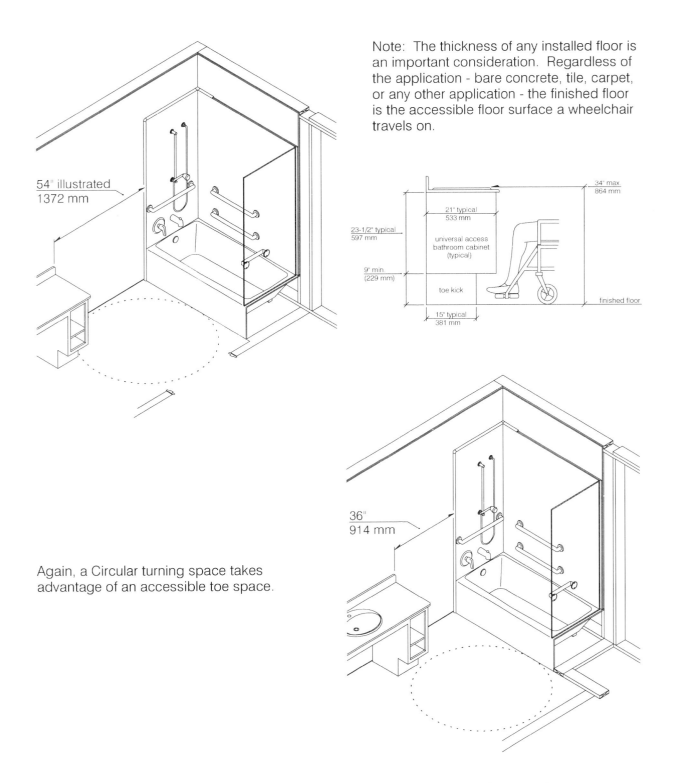

54" illustrated
1372 mm

Note: The thickness of any installed floor is an important consideration. Regardless of the application - bare concrete, tile, carpet, or any other application - the finished floor is the accessible floor surface a wheelchair travels on.

21" typical
533 mm

23-1/2" typical
597 mm

universal access bathroom cabinet (typical)

9" min.
(229 mm)

toe kick

15" typical
381 mm

34" max
864 mm

finished floor

Again, a Circular turning space takes advantage of an accessible toe space.

36"
914 mm

CABINET AND COUNTERTOP NEXT TO A BATHING FIXTURE
Bathtub

A cabinet or countertop cannot obstruct the access to the bathtub/shower controls.

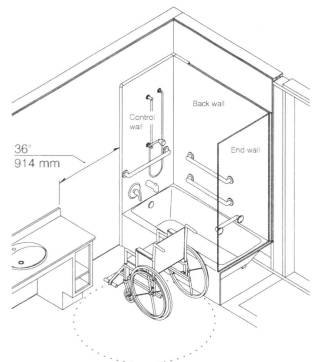

BATHTUB
CLEAR FLOOR SPACE
  a. 30 inches (762 mm) minimum in width.
  b. The depth of the bathtub.

Cabinet and Countertop Position
- A countertop is 36 inches (914 mm) away from a bathtub's control wall.
- A Circular turning space takes advantage of an accessible toe space.

Cabinet and Countertop Position
- A Circular turning space takes advantage of an accessible toe space.

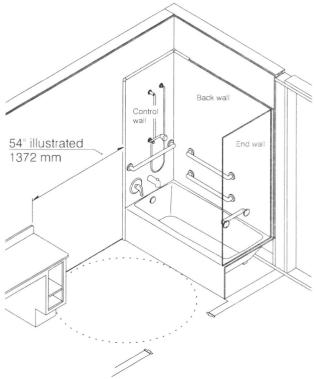

CABINET AND COUNTERTOP NEXT TO A BATHING FIXTURE
Roll-in Shower without Seat

A cabinet or countertop cannot obstruct access to a bathing fixture's controls.

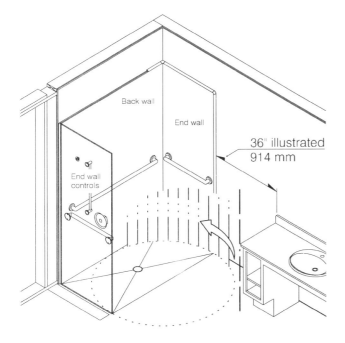

ROLL-IN SHOWER
CLEAR FLOOR SPACE
30 inches (762 mm) minimum in width by 60 inches (1524 mm) minimum in depth adjacent to the shower's open side.

Cabinet and Countertop Position
■ Installed opposite a roll-in shower without seat's end wall controls.

As a general rule, minimum widths and depths should be increased in size wherever space permits.

Cabinet and Countertop Position
■ Installed opposite a roll-in shower without seat's end wall, the end wall closest to the back wall controls.

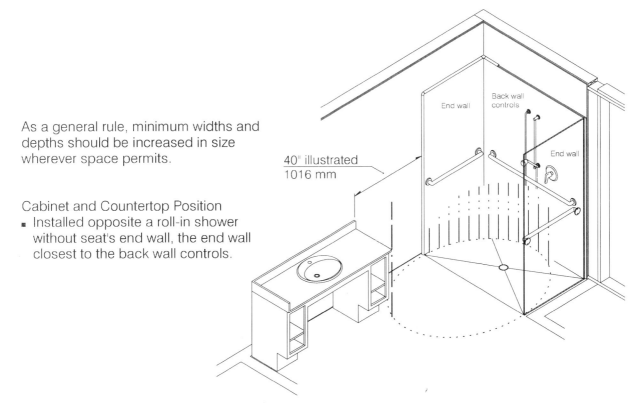

CABINET AND COUNTERTOP NEXT TO A BATHING FIXTURE
Bathing Fixture with Seat

A cabinet or countertop cannot obstruct access to a bathing fixture's controls and seat.

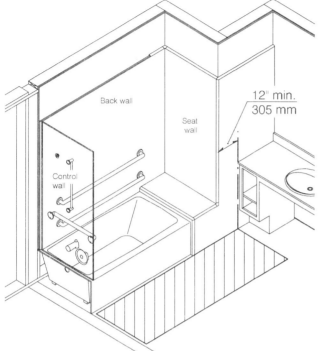

BATHTUB WITH PERMANENT SEAT
CLEAR FLOOR SPACE
a. 30 inches (762 mm) minimum in width.
b. Depth of bathtub and seat and 12 inches (305 mm) beyond the seat wall.

Cabinet and Countertop Position
- A cabinet and countertop are 12 inches beyond a bathtub with permanent seat's seat wall.

ROLL-IN SHOWER
CLEAR FLOOR SPACE
30 inches (762 mm) minimum in width by 60 inches (1524 mm) minimum in depth adjacent to the shower's open side.

Cabinet and Countertop Position
- A cabinet and countertop are installed on the wall opposite a roll-in shower's seat.
- A Circular turning space takes advantage of an accessible toe space.

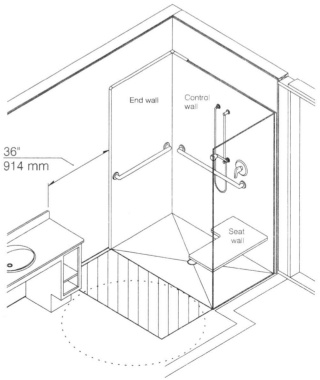

CABINET AND COUNTERTOP NEXT TO A BATHING FIXTURE
Transfer Shower

A cabinet or countertop cannot obstruct access to a bathing fixture's controls and seat.

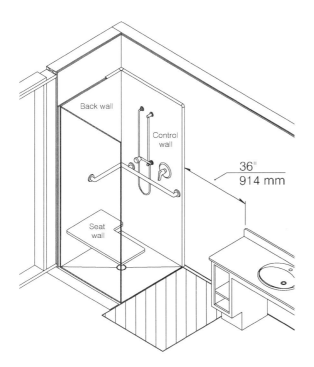

TRANSFER SHOWER
CLEAR FLOOR SPACE
36 inches (914 mm) minimum in width by
48 inches (1219 mm) minimum in depth
measured from the control wall.

Cabinet and Countertop Position
- A countertop is located 36 inches (914 mm) away from the transfer shower's control wall.

Cabinet and Countertop Position
- A countertop does not obstruct a turn to and away from the transfer shower's clear floor space.

Note: The Circular turning space in the picture to the right does not take advantage of an accessible toe space. The Circular turning space, instead, defines the corner of the countertop.

The general rule is, minimum widths and depths should be increased in size wherever space permits.

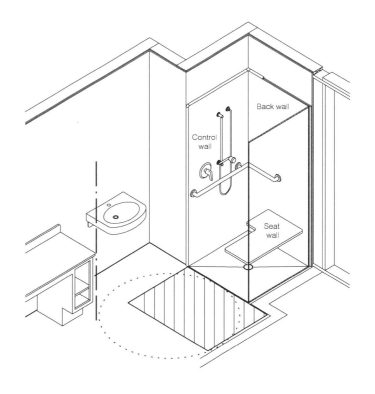

CABINET AND COUNTERTOP NEXT TO A BATHING FIXTURE
Alternate Shower with Seat

A cabinet or countertop cannot obstruct an alternate
shower's entry.

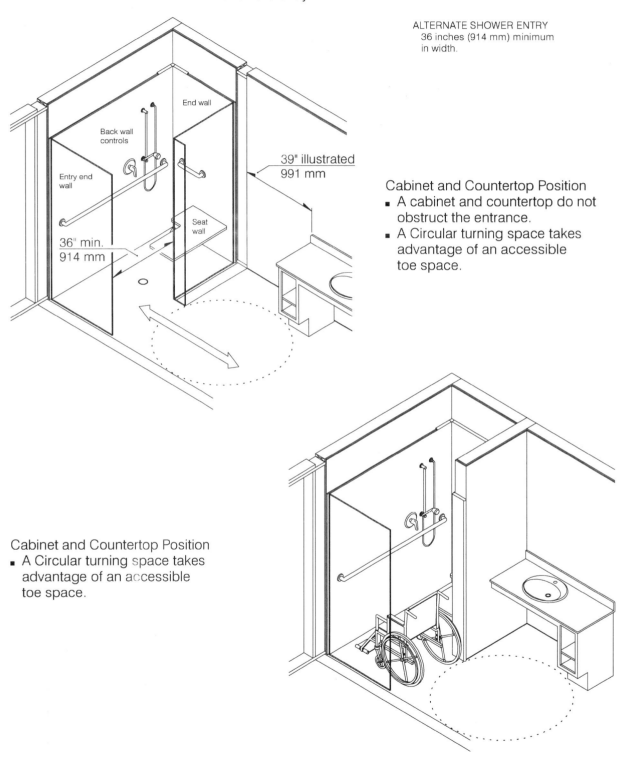

ALTERNATE SHOWER ENTRY
36 inches (914 mm) minimum
in width.

End wall

Back wall
controls

Entry end
wall

Seat
wall

39" illustrated
991 mm

36" min.
914 mm

Cabinet and Countertop Position
- A cabinet and countertop do not
  obstruct the entrance.
- A Circular turning space takes
  advantage of an accessible
  toe space.

Cabinet and Countertop Position
- A Circular turning space takes
  advantage of an accessible
  toe space.

CABINET, COUNTERTOP, AND OVERALL BATHROOM SIZE

When space is limited, it may be necessary to re-examine the advantages of a lavatory versus a cabinet, countertop and sink.

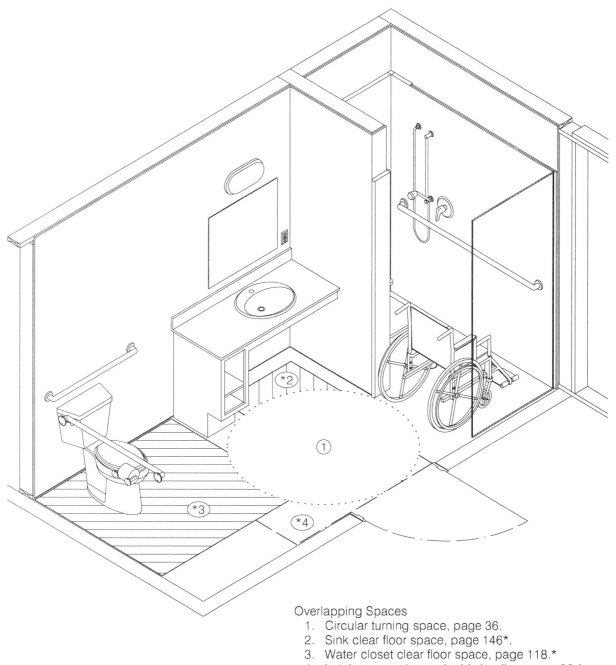

Overlapping Spaces
1. Circular turning space, page 36.
2. Sink clear floor space, page 146*.
3. Water closet clear floor space, page 118.*
4. Latch approach - push side landing, page 92.*

(* partially covered)

NOTES

BATHTUB

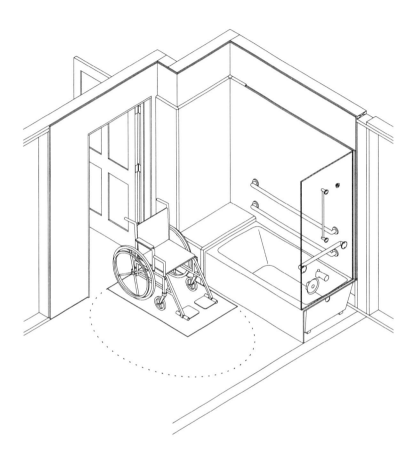

BATHTUB
Design Considerations

Bathtub/shower controls installed on an end wall are part of what makes a bathtub accessible. The list includes a clear floor space, a removable bathing seat, grab bars, and a shower spray unit.

Additional considerations are a turning space and the location of a nearby fixture.

Other views of a bathtub and fixtures:
- Lavatory and bathtub, page 136.
- Cabinet, countertop, and bathtub, page 152.

BATHTUB'S
ADA COMPLIANT FIXTURES

CLEAR FLOOR SPACE
  30 inches (762 mm)
  in width by the depth
  of the bathtub

BATHTUB
1 - 32 inch by 60 inch
  (813 x 1524 mm)
  Bathtub

1 - 12 inch (305 mm)
  End wall grab bar

2 - 24 inch (610 mm)
  Back wall grab bars

1 - 24 inch (610 mm)
  Control wall grab bar

1 - Bathtub/shower controls

1 - Bathtub water spout

1 - Shower spray unit

1 - Removable bathtub seat

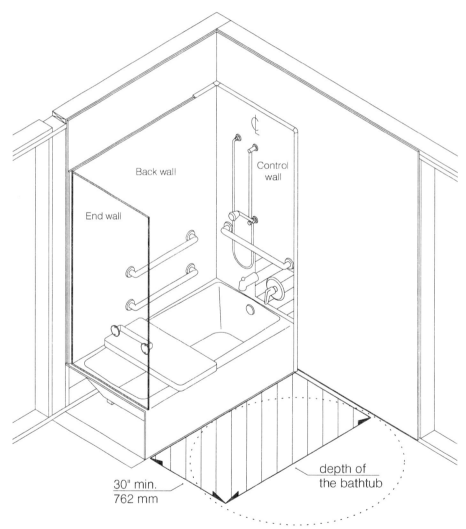

Back wall

Control wall

End wall

30" min.
762 mm

depth of
the bathtub

BATHTUB
Typical Guidelines

END WALL

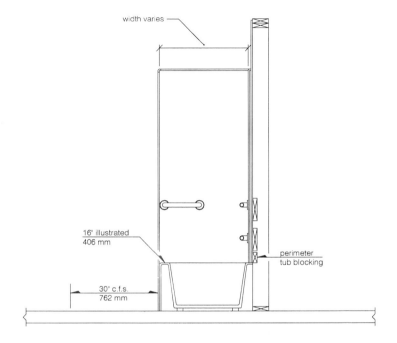

width varies

16" illustrated
406 mm

perimeter
tub blocking

30" c.f.s.
762 mm

BATHTUB
CLEAR FLOOR SPACE
a. 30 inches (762 mm) minimum
    in width.
b. The depth of the bathtub.

BATHTUB WIDTH
Width varies.

■ An illustration is on page 164.

BATHTUB HEIGHT
Height varies.

■ 14 and 16 inches (356 and 406 mm) are
two typical bathtub heights. A 16 inch
tall bathtub may be necessary to attain
a removable seat's minimum height.

BATHTUB DEPTH
Depth varies.

■ An illustration is on page 166.

REMOVABLE SEAT
Capable of secure placement on
the installed bathtub.

REMOVABLE SEAT HEIGHT
17 inches (432 mm) minimum and
19 inches (483 mm) maximum
above the finished floor.

REMOVABLE SEAT DEPTH
15 inches (381 mm) minimum and
16 inches (406 mm) maximum.

BACK WALL

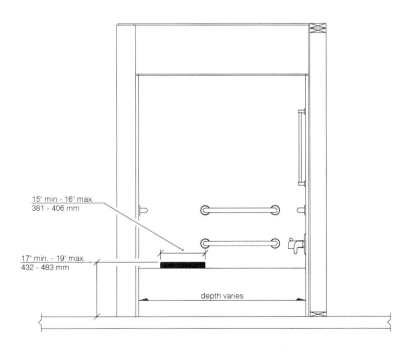

15" min - 16" max.
381 - 406 mm

17" min. - 19" max.
432 - 483 mm

depth varies

BATHTUB
Typical Guidelines

END WALL

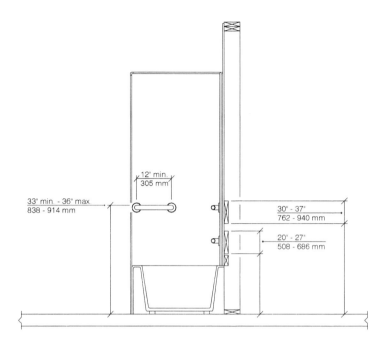

GRAB BAR HEIGHT (typical)
 a. Installed a uniform horizontal height above the finished floor.
 b. 33 inches (838 mm) minimum and 36 inches (914 mm) maximum from the top of the gripping surface to the finished floor.

END WALL GRAB BAR
 a. Typical height.
 b. 12 inches (305 mm) minimum in length.
 c. Installed at the open side of a bathtub.

BACK WALL GRAB BARS
 Upper Grab Bar
  a. Typical height.
  b. 24 inches (610 mm) minimum in length.
  c. 24 inches (610 mm) maximum from the end wall.
  d. 12 inches (305 mm) maximum from the control wall.
 Lower Grab Bar
  a. 8 inches (203 mm) minimum and 10 inches (254 mm) maximum above the bathtub rim.
  b. 24 inches (610 mm) minimum in length.
  c. 24 inches (610 mm) maximum from the end wall.
  d. 12 inches (305 mm) maximum from the control wall.

BACK WALL

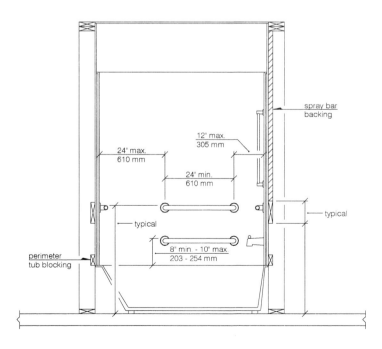

CONTROL WALL GRAB BAR
 a. Typical height.
 b. 24 inches (610 mm) minimum in length.
 c. Installed at the open side of a bathtub.

GRAB BAR BACKING (typical)
 Upper Grab Bars
  30 inches to 37 inches (762 - 940 mm) above the finished floor.
 Lower Grab Bar
  20 inches to 27 inches (508 - 686 mm) above the finished floor.

BATHTUB
Typical Guidelines

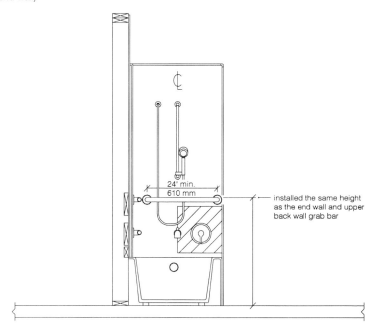

24" min.
610 mm

installed the same height
as the end wall and upper
back wall grab bar

CONTROL WALL

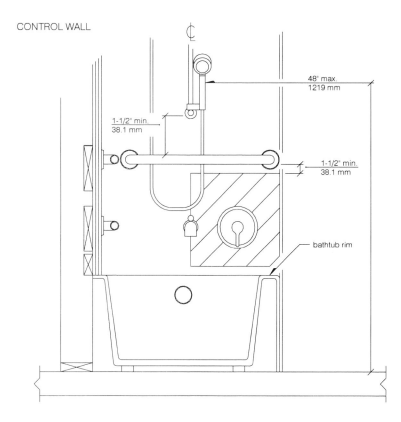

48" max.
1219 mm

1-1/2" min.
38.1 mm

1-1/2" min.
38.1 mm

bathtub rim

BATHTUB
CONTROL WALL

Bathtub/shower controls are installed
on an end wall.

A bathtub's shower spray unit is installed
above the grab bar.

BATHTUB/SHOWER CONTROLS
LOCATION

Centerline and Setback
From the centerline of the control wall
to the open side of the shower.

Centerline Consideration
18 inches (457 mm) maximum
when the control wall is wider
than 36 inches (914 mm).

Maximum Height
1-1/2 inches (38.1 mm) minimum
below the control wall grab bar.

Minimum Height
The bathtub rim.
1-1/2 inches (38.1 mm) above the
rim is illustrated.

BATHTUB
SHOWER SPRAY UNIT

Supply Hose
59 inches (1499 mm) minimum
in length.

Showerhead
Can be used both as a fixed showerhead
and as a handheld showerhead.

Maximum Height
48 inches (1219 mm) maximum
above the finished floor.

Minimum Height
1-1/2 inches (38.1 mm) minimum
above the control wall grab bar.

BATHTUB
Bathing Fixture Width

A 32 inch (813 mm) bathtub with a typical three-ply shower
surround has a width of 30-1/2 inches (775 mm) between
the finished back wall and the open side of this bathtub.
The width is approximate and should be accurate to within
1/4 inch (6.35 mm) given standard board and tiles.

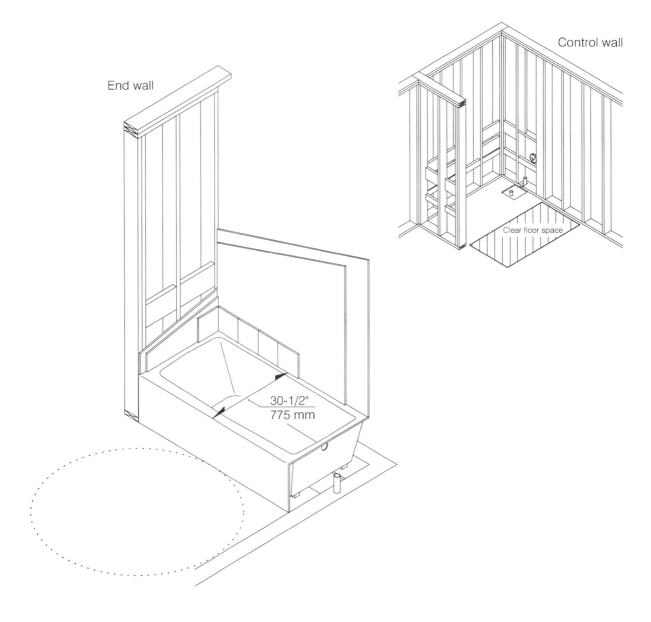

A typical shower surround has three plies.
   1st ply: 1/2 inch (12.7 mm) of water resistant wall board.
   2nd ply: 1/2 inch (12.7 mm) of cement board.
   3rd ply: 1/2 inch (12.7 mm) allowance for mastic and tile.

BATHTUB
  Rough-in Considerations

A bathroom plan should detail:
- Bathtub width, height, depth, and drain location.
- Net thickness of each structural wall and wall covering.
- Grab bar and spray bar backing locations.
- Control valve location.
- Finished floor height.
- Clear floor space.
- Turning space to and away from a bathtub.

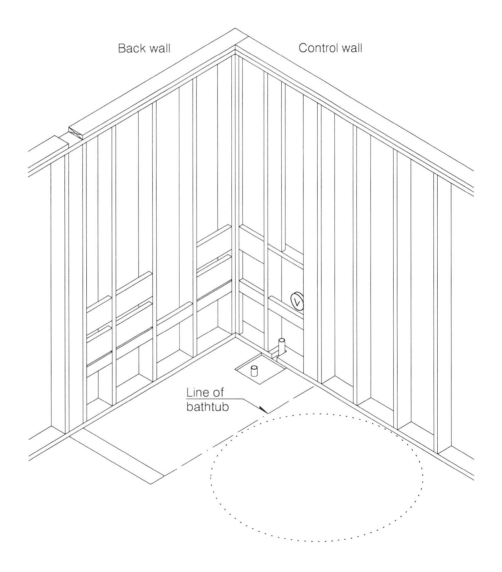

Back wall   Control wall

Line of
bathtub

BATHTUB
Bathing Fixture Depth

A 60 inch (1524 mm) bathtub with a typical three-ply shower
surround has a depth of 57 inches (1448 mm) between
the finished surface of the end wall and the finished surface
of the control wall. The depth is approximate and should be
accurate to within 1/4 inch (6.35 mm) given standard board
and tiles.

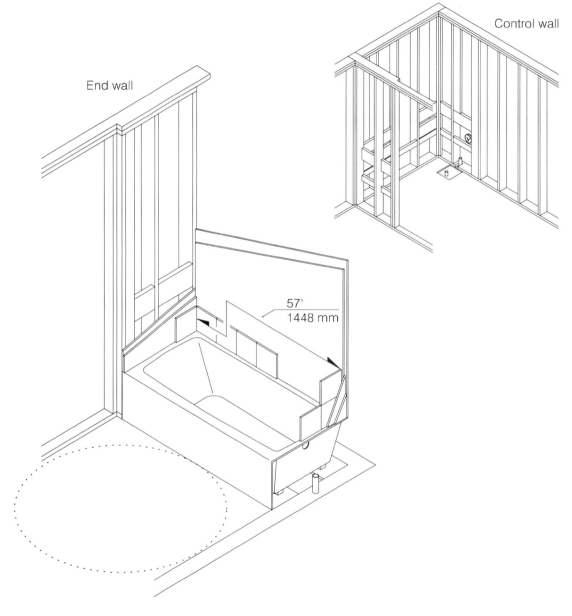

A typical shower surround has three plies.
   1st ply: 1/2 inch (12.7 mm) of water resistant wall board.
   2nd ply: 1/2 inch (12.7 mm) of cement board.
   3rd ply: 1/2 inch (12.7 mm) allowance for mastic and tile.

BATHTUB
Rough-in Considerations

A bathroom plan should detail:
- Bathtub width, height, depth, and drain location.
- Net thickness of each structural wall and wall covering.
- Grab bar and spray bar backing locations.
- Control valve location.
- Finished floor height.
- Clear floor space.
- Turning space to and away from a bathtub.

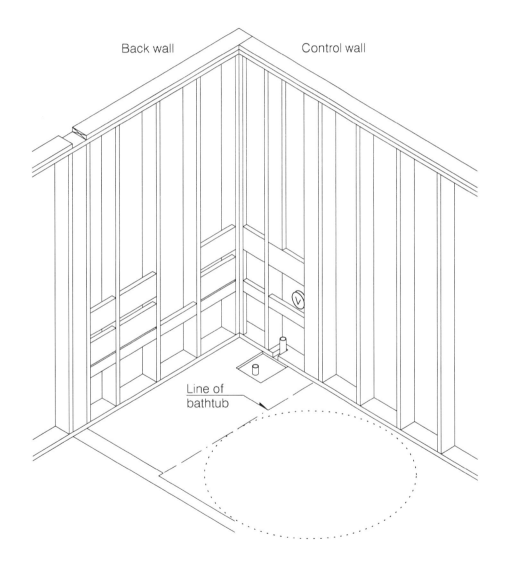

BATHTUB WITH PERMANENT SEAT
Design Considerations

A bathtub with permanent seat's clear floor space is the depth of the bathtub and seat and 12 inches (305 mm) beyond the seat wall. This length is an important planning consideration.

The clear floor space width and the location of a nearby fixture are also important considerations.

Other views of a bathtub with permanent seat and fixtures:
- Lavatory and bathing fixture with seat, page 138.
- Cabinet, countertop, and bathing fixture with seat, page 154.

BATHTUB WITH PERMANENT SEAT'S
ADA COMPLIANT FIXTURES

CLEAR FLOOR SPACE
    30 inches (762 mm) in width by the depth of the bathtub and seat and 12 inches beyond the seat wall

BATHTUB
1 - 32 inch by 60 inch (813 x 1524 mm) Bathtub

1 - 15 inch (381 mm) deep Permanent seat

2 - 48 inch (1219 mm) Back wall grab bars

1 - 24 inch (610 mm) Control wall grab bar

1 - Bathtub/shower controls

1 - Bathtub water spout

1 - Shower spray unit

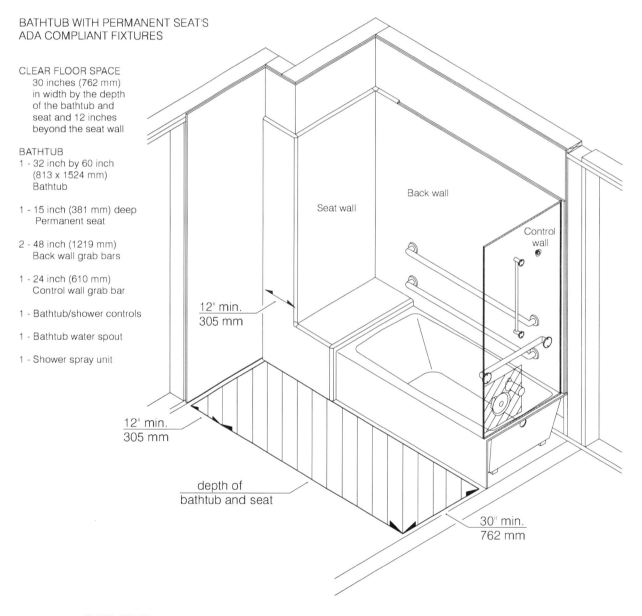

Back wall

Seat wall

Control wall

12" min.
305 mm

12" min.
305 mm

depth of bathtub and seat

30" min.
762 mm

BATHTUB WITH PERMANENT SEAT
Typical Guidelines

CLEAR FLOOR SPACE

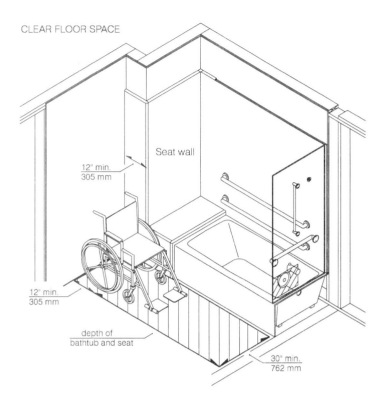

Seat wall

12" min.
305 mm

12" min.
305 mm

depth of
bathtub and seat

30" min.
762 mm

BACK WALL

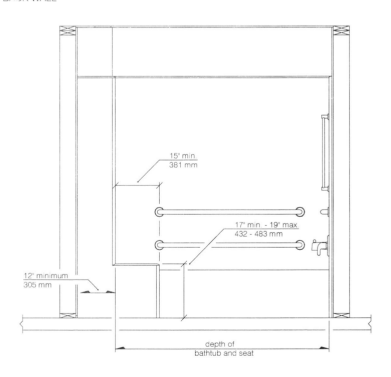

15" min.
381 mm

17" min - 19" max.
432 - 483 mm

12" minimum
305 mm

depth of
bathtub and seat

BATHTUB WITH PERMANENT SEAT
CLEAR FLOOR SPACE
   a. 30 inches (762 mm) minimum
       in width.
   b. Depth of bathtub and seat and
       12 inches (305 mm) beyond the
       seat wall.

BATHTUB WIDTH
   Width varies.

   ▪ An illustration is on page 164.

BATHTUB HEIGHT
   Height varies.

   ▪ 14 and 16 inches (356 and 406 mm)
     are two typical bathtub heights.

BATHTUB AND SEAT DEPTH
   Depth of bathtub and seat varies.

   ▪ A picture illustrating bathroom size
     is on page 172.

PERMANENT SEAT WIDTH
   From the back wall to the open side
   of the bathtub or seat.

PERMANENT SEAT HEIGHT
   17 inches (432 mm) minimum and
   19 inches (483 mm) maximum
   above the finished floor.

PERMANENT SEAT DEPTH
   15 inches (381 mm) minimum
   from the seat wall.

BATHTUB WITH PERMANENT SEAT
Typical Guidelines

SEAT WALL

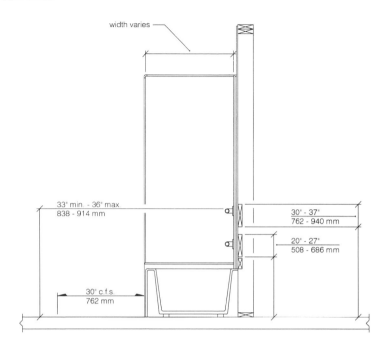

GRAB BAR HEIGHT (typical)
  a. Installed a uniform horizontal height above the finished floor.
  b. 33 inches (838 mm) minimum and 36 inches (914 mm) maximum from the top of the gripping surface to the finished floor.

BACK WALL GRAB BARS
  Upper Grab Bar
    a. Typical height.
    b. The depth of the bathtub and seat determines the length.
    c. 15 inches (381 mm) maximum from the seat wall.
    d. 12 inches (305 mm) maximum from the control wall.
  Lower Grab Bar
    a. 8 inches (203 mm) minimum and 10 inches (254 mm) maximum above the bathtub rim.
    b. The depth of the bathtub and seat determines the length.
    c. 15 inches (610 mm) maximum from the seat wall.
    d. 12 inches (305 mm) maximum from the control wall.

    ■ 2 - 48 inch (1219 mm) grab bars are illustrated.

CONTROL WALL GRAB BAR
  a. Typical height.
  b. 24 inches (610 mm) minimum in length.
  c. Installed at the open side of a bathtub.

GRAB BAR BACKING (typical)
  Upper Grab Bars
    30 inches to 37 inches (762 - 940 mm) above the finished floor.
  Lower Grab Bar
    20 inches to 27 inches (508 - 686 mm) above the finished floor.

BACK WALL

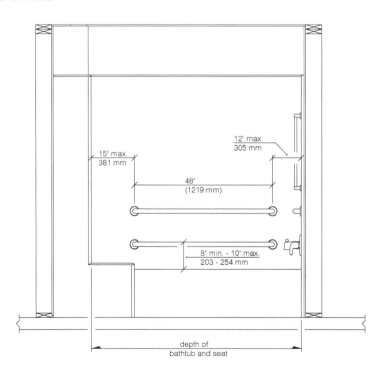

BATHTUB WITH PERMANENT SEAT
Typical Guidelines

CONTROL WALL
(end wall)

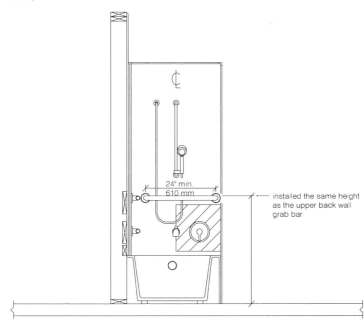

24" min.
610 mm

installed the same height
as the upper back wall
grab bar

CONTROL WALL

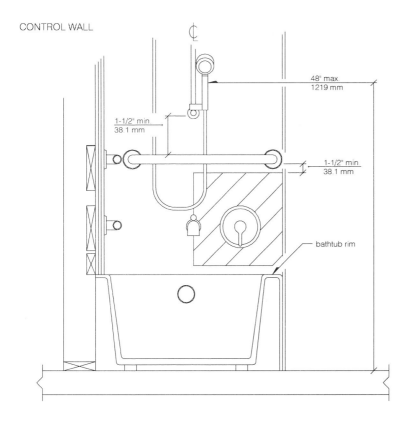

48" max.
1219 mm

1-1/2" min.
38.1 mm

1-1/2" min.
38.1 mm

bathtub rim

BATHTUB
CONTROL WALL

Bathtub/shower controls are installed
on an end wall.

A bathtub's shower spray unit is installed
above the grab bar.

BATHTUB/SHOWER CONTROLS
LOCATION

Centerline and Setback
From the centerline of the control wall
to the open side of the shower.

Centerline Consideration
18 inches (457 mm) maximum
when the control wall is wider
than 36 inches (914 mm).

Maximum Height
1-1/2 inches (38.1 mm) minimum
below the control wall grab bar.

Minimum Height
The bathtub rim.
1-1/2 inches (38.1 mm) above the
rim is illustrated.

BATHTUB
SHOWER SPRAY UNIT

Supply Hose
59 inches (1499 mm) minimum
in length.

Showerhead
Can be used both as a fixed showerhead
and as a handheld showerhead.

Maximum Height
48 inches (1219 mm) maximum
above the finished floor.

Minimum Height
1-1/2 inches (38.1 mm) minimum
above the control wall grab bar.

BATHTUB WITH PERMANENT SEAT
Bathroom Size

When a bathtub with permanent seat is between unfinished wall X and unfinished wall Y, the minimum rough opening is found by adding together:
1. Building material on wall X, typically 1/2 inch (12.7 mm).
2. At minimum, 12 inches (305 mm) beyond the seat wall.
3. Length of the permanent seat and bathtub.

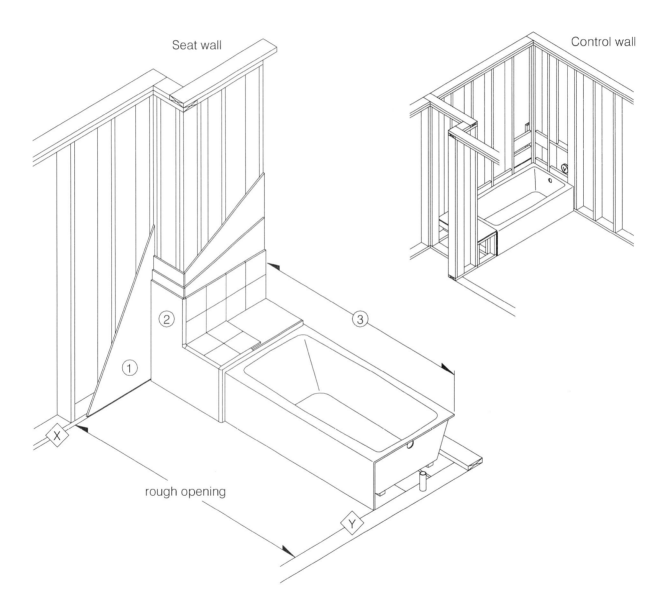

Seat wall

Control wall

rough opening

X

Y

A typical shower surround has three plies.
1st ply: 1/2 inch (12.7 mm) of water resistant wall board.
2nd ply: 1/2 inch (12.7 mm) of cement board.
3rd ply: 1/2 inch (12.7 mm) allowance for mastic and tile.

BATHTUB WITH PERMANENT SEAT
Rough-in Considerations

A bathroom plan should detail:
- Bathtub width, height, depth, and drain location.
- Net thickness of each structural wall and wall covering.
- Seat width, height, and depth.
- Grab bar and spray bar backing locations.
- Control valve location.
- Finished floor height.
- Clear floor space.
- Turning space to and away from a bathtub with permanent seat.

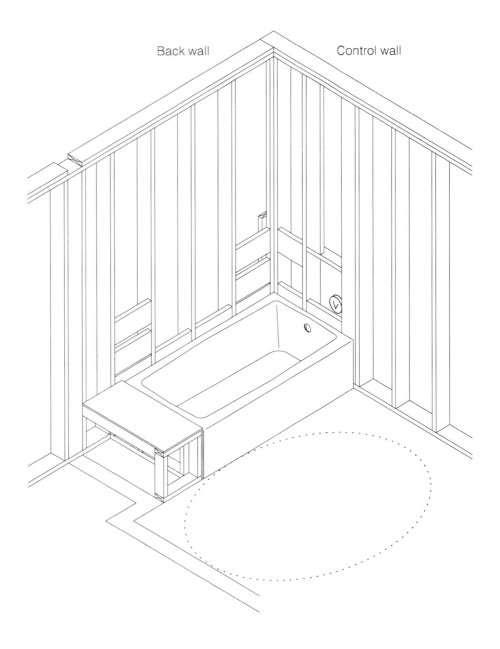

NOTES

ROLL-IN SHOWER

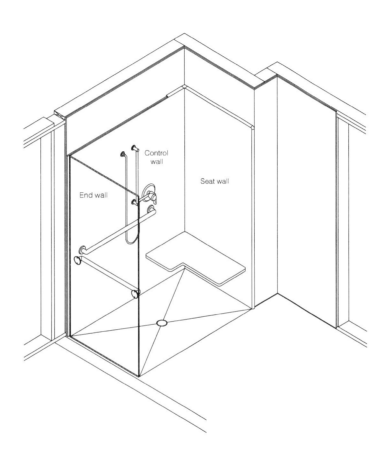

ROLL-IN SHOWER WITHOUT SEAT
Design Considerations

An important consideration is a roll-in shower's size. It has a minimum width and a minimum depth. Another consideration is the control wall. A roll-in shower without seat's controls and shower spray unit are installed on either an end wall or installed on the back wall. End wall controls are pictured below.

The change in level from the bathroom floor to the shower floor is another important consideration.

Other views of a roll-in shower and fixtures:
- Lavatory and roll-in shower without seat, page 137.
- Cabinet, countertop, and roll-in shower without seat, page 153.

ROLL-IN SHOWER WITHOUT SEAT'S
ADA COMPLIANT FIXTURES

CLEAR FLOOR SPACE
30 inch by 60 inch
(762 x 1524 mm)
Roll-in shower
clear floor space

ROLL-IN SHOWER
1 - 30 inch by 60 inch
(762 x 1524 mm)
Roll-in shower

2 - 24 inch (610 mm)
End wall grab bars

1 - 48 inch (1219 mm)
Back wall grab bar

1 - Shower controls

1 - Shower spray unit

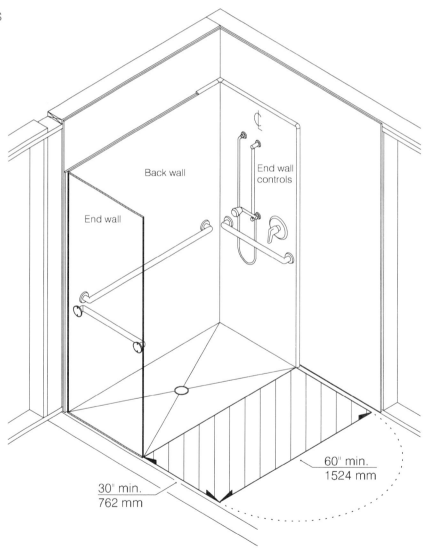

Back wall

End wall controls

End wall

60" min.
1524 mm

30" min.
762 mm

ROLL-IN SHOWER WITHOUT SEAT
Typical Guidelines

END WALL

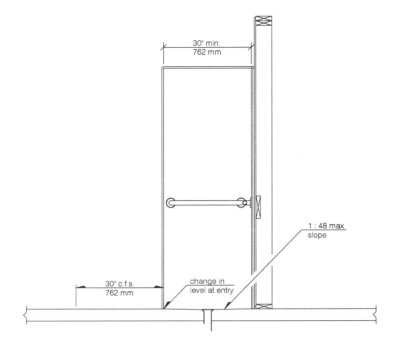

ROLL-IN SHOWER
CLEAR FLOOR SPACE
30 inches (762 mm) minimum in width by
60 inches (1524 mm) minimum in depth
adjacent to the shower's open side.

ROLL-IN SHOWER WIDTH
30 inches (762 mm) minimum
from the back wall to the open side
of the shower.

ROLL-IN SHOWER DEPTH
60 inches (1524 mm) minimum
from end wall to end wall.

BACK WALL

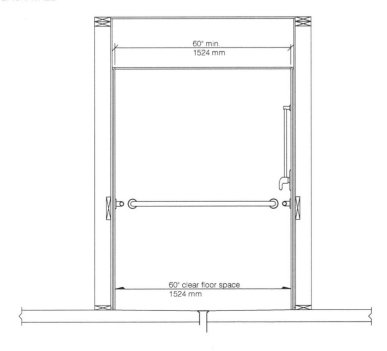

SHOWER FLOOR TO BATHROOM FLOOR
CHANGE IN LEVEL
a. One-quarter inch (6.35 mm) maximum
vertical change in level.
b. One-half inch (12.7 mm) maximum
beveled change in level.

SHOWER FLOOR SLOPE
1 : 48 maximum cross slope and
running slope.

ROLL-IN SHOWER WITHOUT SEAT
Typical Guidelines

END WALL

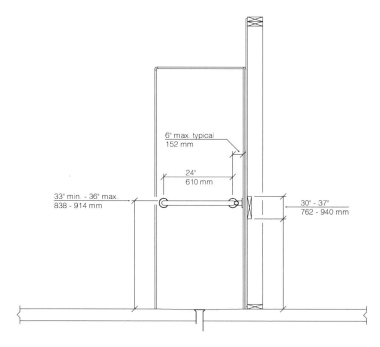

6" max. typical
152 mm

24"
610 mm

33" min. - 36" max.
838 - 914 mm

30" - 37"
762 - 940 mm

GRAB BAR HEIGHT (typical)
a. Installed a uniform horizontal height above the finished floor.
b. 33 inches (838 mm) minimum and 36 inches (914 mm) maximum from the top of the gripping surface to the shower's finished floor.

END WALL GRAB BARS
a. Typical height.
b. The shower's width determines the grab bars' length.
c. 6 inches (152 mm) maximum from the back wall.
d. Installed near the open side of the shower.

■ 24 inch (610 mm) grab bars are illustrated.

BACK WALL

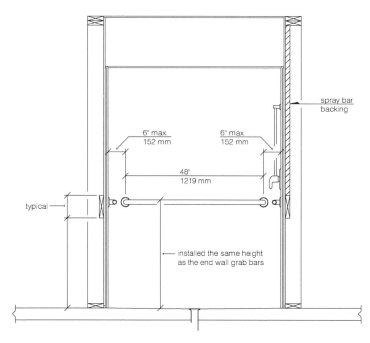

spray bar backing

6" max
152 mm

6" max
152 mm

48"
1219 mm

typical

installed the same height as the end wall grab bars

BACK WALL GRAB BAR
a. Typical height.
b. The shower's depth determines the grab bar's length.
c. 6 inches (152 mm) maximum from either end wall.

■ A 48 inch (1219 mm) grab bar is illustrated.

GRAB BAR BACKING (typical)
30 inches to 37 inches (762 - 940 mm) above the finished floor.

ROLL-IN SHOWER WITHOUT SEAT
Typical Guidelines

CONTROL WALL
(back wall controls)

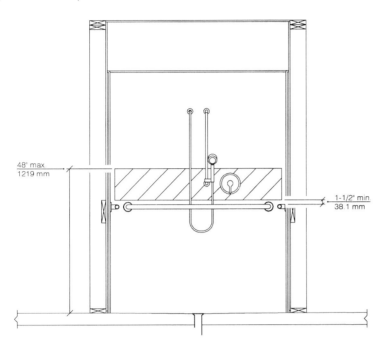

48" max
1219 mm

1-1/2" min
38.1 mm

CONTROL WALL
(end wall controls)

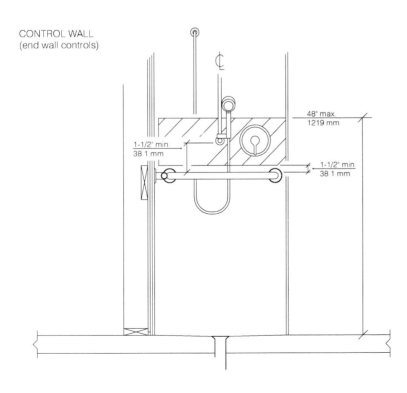

48" max.
1219 mm

1-1/2" min
38.1 mm

1-1/2" min.
38.1 mm

ROLL-IN SHOWER WITHOUT SEAT
CONTROL WALL

A roll-in shower without seat's controls
and shower spray unit are installed either
on an end wall or installed on the back wall.

CONTROLS AND SHOWER SPRAY UNIT
END WALL AND BACK WALL LOCATION

Maximum Height
48 inches (1219 mm) maximum
above the shower's finished floor.

Minimum Height
1-1/2 inches (38.1 mm) minimum
above the grab bar.

SHOWER SPRAY UNIT

Supply Hose
59 inches (1499 mm) minimum
in length.

Showerhead
Can be used both as a fixed showerhead
and as a handheld showerhead.

ROLL-IN SHOWER WITHOUT SEAT
Bathroom Size

When a roll-in shower is between unfinished wall X
and unfinished wall Y, the minimum rough opening
is found by adding together:
1.   The building materials on both end walls, typically
     3 inches (76.2 mm).
2.   The roll-in shower's minimum depth.

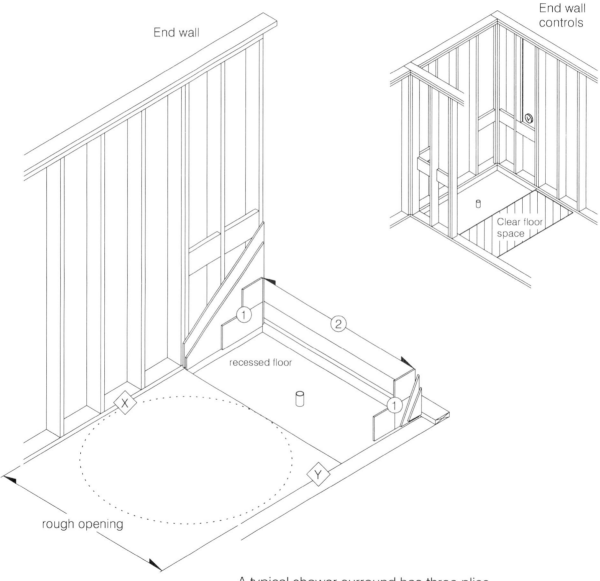

A typical shower surround has three plies.
   1st ply: 1/2 inch (12.7 mm) of water resistant wall board.
   2nd ply: 1/2 inch (12.7 mm) of cement board.
   3rd ply: 1/2 inch (12.7 mm) allowance for mastic and tile.

ROLL-IN SHOWER WITHOUT SEAT
Rough-in Considerations

A bathroom plan should detail:
- Roll-in shower width, depth, and drain location.
- Net thickness of each structural wall and wall covering.
- Grab bar and spray bar backing locations.
- Control valve location.
- Clear floor space.
- Recessed floor, built-up floor, and shower floor assembly detailing drainage and an accessible transition to the bathroom floor.
- All finished floor heights.
- Turning space to and away from a roll-in shower.

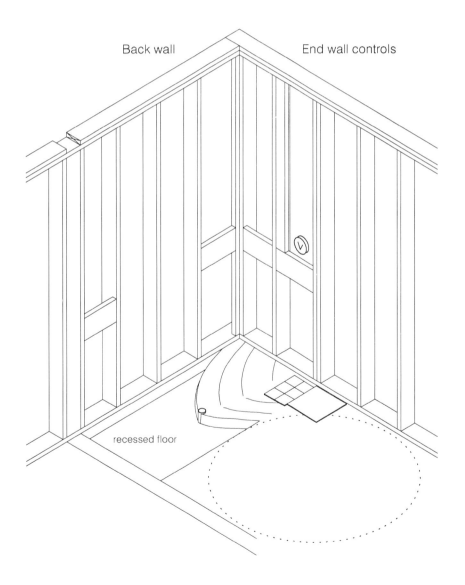

Back wall   End wall controls

recessed floor

ROLL-IN SHOWER WITH SEAT
  Design Considerations

A roll-in shower with seat's controls and shower spray unit
are installed on the back wall adjacent to a rectangular or
an L - shaped seat.

The roll-in shower illustrated below has a 36 inch (914 mm) wide
seat wall. This seat wall is wide enough for a transfer shower size
L - shaped folding seat.

Important considerations are a turning space, any maneuvering
space beyond the seat wall, and the location of a nearby fixture.

Other views of a roll-in shower and fixtures:
  ▪ Lavatory and bathing fixture with seat, page 138.
  ▪ Cabinet, countertop, and bathing fixture with seat, page 154.

ROLL-IN SHOWER WITH SEAT'S
ADA COMPLIANT FIXTURES

CLEAR FLOOR SPACE
  30 inch by 60 inch
  (762 x 1524 mm)
  Roll-in shower
  clear floor space

ROLL-IN SHOWER
1 - 36 inch x 60 inch
  (914 x 1524mm)
  Roll-in shower

1 - Transfer shower size
  L - shaped folding seat

1 - Shower controls

1 - Shower spray unit

1 - 36 inch (914 mm)
  Control wall grab bar

1 - 30 inch (762 mm)
  End wall grab bar

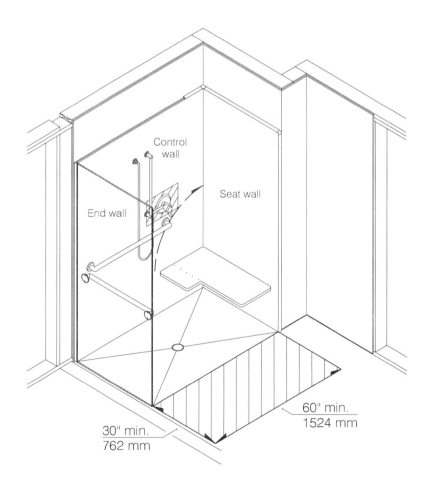

Control
wall

Seat wall

End wall

60" min.
1524 mm

30" min.
762 mm

Note: An L - shaped folding seat must have a clear path
as it folds up past an adjacent grab bar. Coordinating the
grab bar's height and length with a folding seat's height
ensures a clear path to the seat wall. An example is on
page 184.

ROLL-IN SHOWER WITH SEAT
Typical Guidelines

SEAT WALL

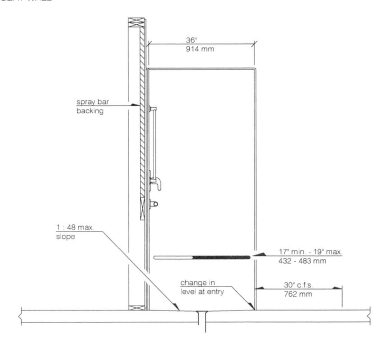

36"
914 mm

spray bar
backing

1 : 48 max.
slope

17" min. - 19" max.
432 - 483 mm

change in
level at entry

30" c.f.s.
762 mm

CONTROL WALL
(back wall)

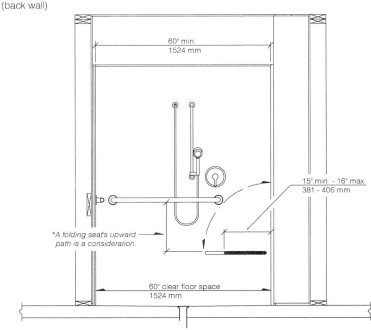

60" min.
1524 mm

15" min. - 16" max.
381 - 406 mm

*A folding seat's upward
path is a consideration.

60" clear floor space
1524 mm

ROLL-IN SHOWER
CLEAR FLOOR SPACE
30 inches (762 mm) minimum in width by
60 inches (1524 mm) minimum in depth
adjacent to the shower's open side.

ROLL-IN SHOWER WIDTH
30 inches (762 mm) minimum
from the control wall (back wall)
to the open side of the shower.

- A 36 inch wide shower is a more
  practical space to bathe in and is
  wide enough for a transfer shower
  size L - shaped folding seat.

ROLL-IN SHOWER DEPTH
60 inches (1524 mm) minimum
from the end wall to the seat wall.

SHOWER FLOOR TO BATHROOM FLOOR
CHANGE IN LEVEL
a. One-quarter inch (6.35 mm) maximum
   vertical change in level.
b. One-half inch (12.7 mm) maximum
   beveled change in level.

SHOWER FLOOR SLOPE
1 : 48 maximum cross slope and
running slope.

SEAT WIDTH
Must comply with the open side setback
and the adjacent side setback.

- Both setbacks are on page 208.

SEAT HEIGHT
17 inches (432 mm) minimum and
19 inches (483 mm) maximum
above the shower's finished floor.

*The space between a folding seat's
L portion and the control wall grab bar
is a consideration. An example is on
page 184.

SEAT DEPTH
15 inches (381 mm) minimum and
16 inches (406 mm) maximum
from the seat wall.

ROLL-IN SHOWER WITH SEAT
Typical Guidelines

END WALL

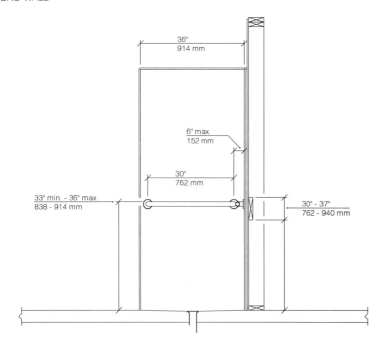

36"
914 mm

6" max.
152 mm

30"
762 mm

33" min. - 36" max.
838 - 914 mm

30" - 37"
762 - 940 mm

GRAB BAR HEIGHT (typical)
a. Installed a uniform horizontal height above the finished floor.
b. 33 inches (838 mm) minimum and 36 inches (914 mm) maximum from the top of the gripping surface to the shower's finished floor.

Note the control wall grab bar's height and length considerations below.

END WALL GRAB BAR
a. The same height as the control wall grab bar.
b. The shower's width determines the grab bar's length.
c. 6 inches (152 mm) maximum from the control wall.
d. Installed near the open side of a roll-in shower.

    ■ A 30 inch (762 mm) grab bar is illustrated.

CONTROL WALL GRAB BAR
a. Grab bars are not installed above the seat.
b. Height and Length - An L - shaped folding seat must have a clear path as it folds up past an adjacent grab bar. Coordinating the grab bar's height and length with a folding seat's height ensures a clear path to the seat wall.
c. 6 inches (152 mm) maximum from the end wall.

    ■ A 36 inch (914 mm) grab bar is illustrated.

GRAB BAR BACKING (typical)
30 inches to 37 inches (762 - 940 mm) above the finished floor.

SEAT BACKING
Solid blocking from the finished floor to a point near the top of the seat.

    ■ 18 inches (457 mm) above the finished floor is illustrated.

CONTROL WALL
(back wall)

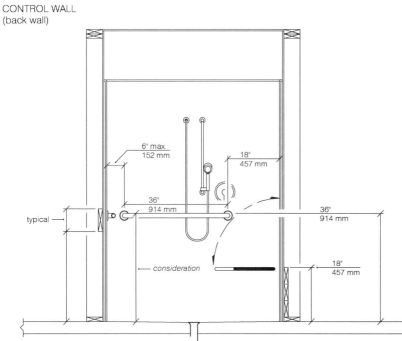

6" max.
152 mm

18"
457 mm

36"
914 mm

typical

36"
914 mm

— consideration

18"
457 mm

ROLL-IN SHOWER WITH SEAT
Typical Guidelines

SEAT WALL

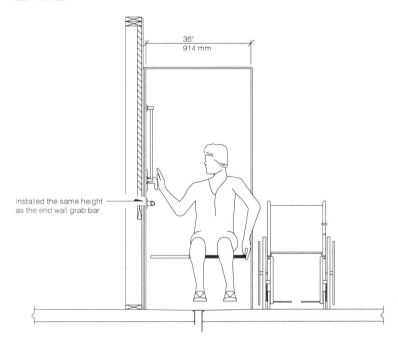

36"
914 mm

Installed the same height
as the end wall grab bar

CONTROL WALL
(back wall)

27" max
686 mm

*12"
305 mm

48" max
1219 mm

1-1/2" min
38.1 mm

1-1/2" min.
38.1 mm

ROLL-IN SHOWER WITH SEAT
CONTROL WALL

A roll-in shower with seat's controls
and shower spray unit are installed
on the back wall adjacent to a seat.

CONTROLS AND SHOWER SPRAY UNIT
LOCATION

Seat Wall Setback
27 inches (686 mm) maximum
from the seat wall.

*Seat Wall Setback Consideration
As an L - shaped seat folds up,
the L portion must have a clear
path past the grab bar, controls,
and a shower spray unit. Reach
is also a consideration.

Maximum Height
48 inches (1219 mm) maximum
above the shower's finished floor.

Minimum Height
1-1/2 inches (38.1 mm) minimum
above the control wall grab bar.

SHOWER SPRAY UNIT

Supply Hose
59 inches (1499 mm) minimum
in length.

Showerhead
Can be used both as a fixed showerhead
and as a handheld showerhead.

ROLL-IN SHOWER WITH SEAT
Bathroom Size

When a roll-in shower with seat and additional maneuvering space are between unfinished wall X and unfinished wall Y, the rough opening is found by adding together:

1. Wall board thickness on wall Y.
2. Maneuvering space beyond the seat wall.
3. A roll-in shower's minimum depth.
4. Building materials on the shower's end wall, typically 1-1/2 inches (38.1 mm).

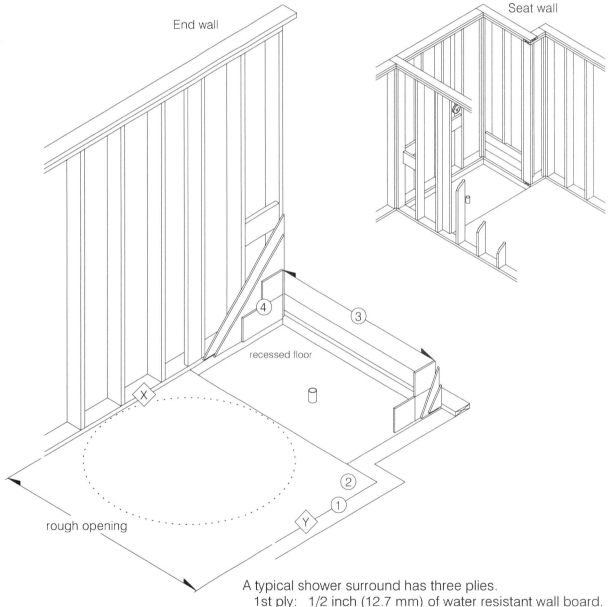

End wall

Seat wall

recessed floor

rough opening

A typical shower surround has three plies.
1st ply: 1/2 inch (12.7 mm) of water resistant wall board.
2nd ply: 1/2 inch (12.7 mm) of cement board.
3rd ply: 1/2 inch (12.7 mm) allowance for mastic and tile.

ROLL-IN SHOWER WITH SEAT
Rough-in Considerations

A bathroom plan should detail:
- Roll-in shower width, depth, and drain location.
- Net thickness of each structural wall and wall covering.
- Grab bar, spray bar, and seat backing locations.
- Control valve location.
- Maneuvering space beyond the seat wall.
- Clear floor space.
- Recessed floor, built-up floor, and shower floor assembly detailing drainage and an accessible transition to the bathroom floor.
- All finished floor heights.
- Turning space to and away from a roll-in shower with seat.

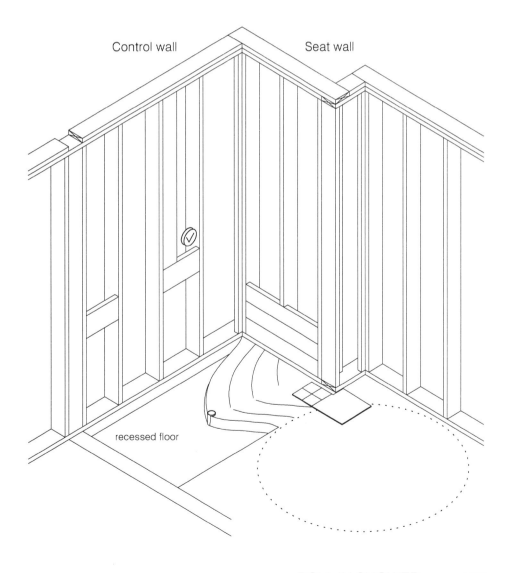

Control wall   Seat wall

recessed floor

NOTES

TRANSFER AND ALTERNATE SHOWER

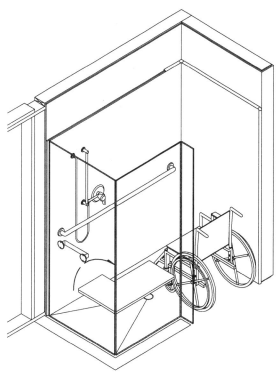

PAGE

TRANSFER SHOWER
  Design Considerations

A transfer shower is 36 inches wide and 36 inches deep
(914 x 914 mm). This shower's controls and shower spray
unit are installed on the wall opposite a rectangular or an
L - shaped seat.

Typically, a transfer shower is pictured with an L - shaped
folding seat. Up, a folding seat gives this shower dual use.

Other views of a transfer shower, turning space, and fixtures:
  ▪ Lavatory and transfer shower, page 139.
  ▪ Cabinet, countertop, and transfer shower, page 155.

TRANSFER SHOWER'S
ADA COMPLIANT FIXTURES

CLEAR FLOOR SPACE
   36 inch by 48 inch
   (914 x 1219 mm)
   Transfer shower
   clear floor space

TRANSFER SHOWER
1 - 36 inch by 36 inch
   (914 x 914 mm)
   Transfer shower

1 - L - shaped folding seat

1 - 33 inch by 18 inch
   (838 x 457 mm)
   L - shaped grab bar

1 - Shower controls

1 - Shower spray unit

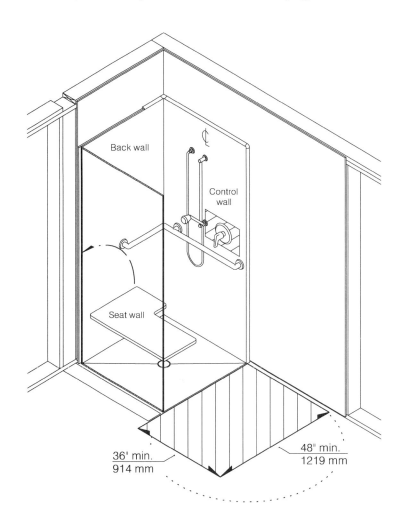

Note: An L - shaped folding seat must have a clear path as it
folds up past an adjacent grab bar. Coordinating the grab bar's
height and length with a folding seat's height ensures a clear path
to the seat wall. An example is on page 192.

TRANSFER SHOWER
Typical Guidelines

SEAT WALL

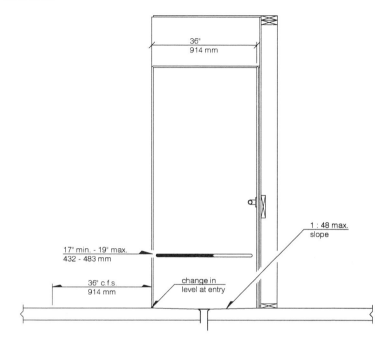

36"
914 mm

1 : 48 max.
slope

17" min. - 19" max.
432 - 483 mm

36" c.f.s.
914 mm

change in
level at entry

BACK WALL

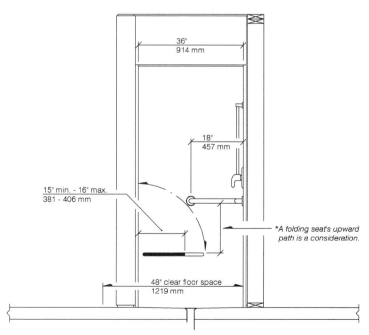

36"
914 mm

18"
457 mm

15" min. - 16" max.
381 - 406 mm

*A folding seat's upward
path is a consideration.

48" clear floor space
1219 mm

TRANSFER SHOWER
CLEAR FLOOR SPACE
36 inches (914 mm) minimum in width by
48 inches (1219 mm) minimum in depth
measured from the control wall.

TRANSFER SHOWER WIDTH
36 inches (914 mm) from the back wall
to the open side of the shower.

TRANSFER SHOWER DEPTH
36 inches (914 mm) from the seat wall
to the control wall.

SHOWER FLOOR TO BATHROOM FLOOR
CHANGE IN LEVEL
One-half inch (12.7 mm) maximum vertical,
beveled, or rounded change in level.

SHOWER FLOOR SLOPE
1 : 48 maximum cross slope and
running slope.

SEAT WIDTH
Must comply with the open side setback
and the adjacent side setback.

■ Both setbacks are on page 208.

SEAT HEIGHT
17 inches (432 mm) minimum and
19 inches (483 mm) maximum
above the shower's finished floor.

*The space between a folding seat's
L portion and the back wall grab bar
is a consideration. An example is on
page 192.

SEAT DEPTH
15 inches (381 mm) minimum and
16 inches (406 mm) maximum
from the seat wall.

TRANSFER SHOWER
Typical Guidelines

SEAT WALL

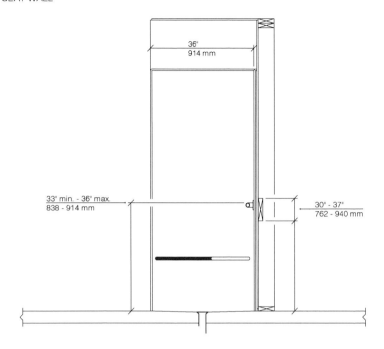

GRAB BAR HEIGHT (typical)
a. Installed a uniform horizontal height above the finished floor.
b. 33 inches (838 mm) minimum and 36 inches (914 mm) maximum from the top of the gripping surface to the shower's finished floor.

Note the back wall grab bar's height consideration below.

BACK WALL LEG OF AN L - SHAPED GRAB BAR
a. Height - An L - shaped folding seat must have a clear path as it folds up past an adjacent grab bar. Coordinating this grab bar's height with a folding seat's height ensures a clear path to the seat wall.
b. Length - To a point 18 inches from the control wall.

CONTROL WALL LEG OF AN L - SHAPED GRAB BAR
a. Height - The same as the back wall leg.
b. Length - The length extends to a point near the open side of the shower.

  ■ A 33 inch (838 mm) leg is illustrated.

BACK WALL

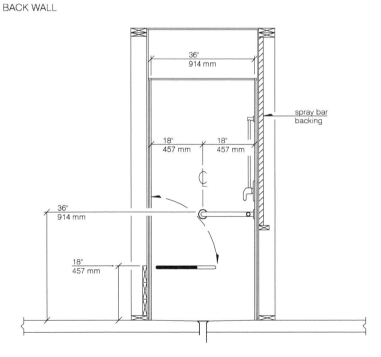

GRAB BAR BACKING (typical)
30 inches to 37 inches (762 - 940 mm) above the finished floor.

SEAT BACKING
Solid blocking from the finished floor to a point near the top of the seat.

  ■ 18 inches (457 mm) above the finished floor is illustrated.

TRANSFER SHOWER
Typical Guidelines

CONTROL WALL

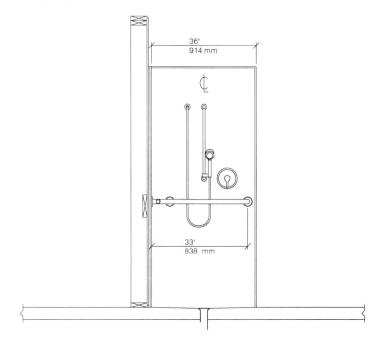

CONTROL WALL

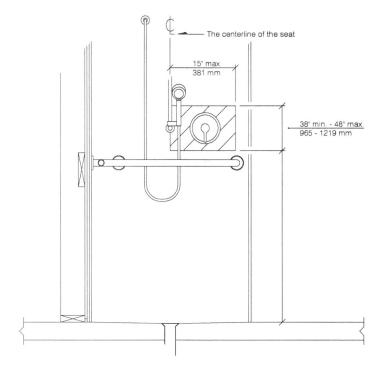

TRANSFER SHOWER
CONTROL WALL

The transfer shower's controls and
shower spray unit are installed on
the wall opposite the seat.

CONTROLS AND SHOWER SPRAY UNIT
LOCATION

Centerline and Setback
The centerline of the seat to
15 inches (381 mm) maximum
from the centerline on the open
side of the shower.

Maximum Height
48 inches (1219 mm) maximum
above the shower's finished floor.

Minimum Height
38 inches (965 mm) minimum
above the shower's finished floor.

SHOWER SPRAY UNIT

Supply Hose
59 inches (1499 mm) minimum
in length.

Showerhead
Can be used both as a fixed showerhead
and as a handheld showerhead.

TRANSFER SHOWER
Bathroom Size

A Circular turning space should be the minimum maneuvering space in and away from a transfer shower.

Below, the control wall end of the clear floor space defines a circular turning space. On the next page, the seat wall end of the clear floor space defines a circular turning space.

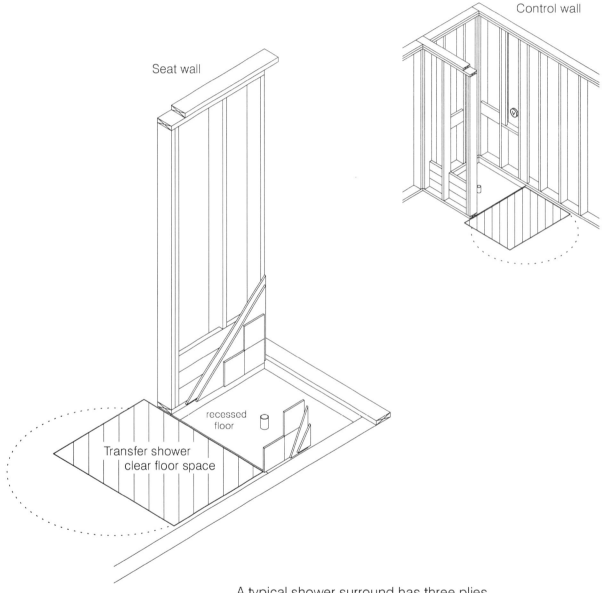

Seat wall

Control wall

recessed floor

Transfer shower clear floor space

A typical shower surround has three plies.
    1st ply: 1/2 inch (12.7 mm) of water resistant wall board.
    2nd ply: 1/2 inch (12.7 mm) of cement board.
    3rd ply: 1/2 inch (12.7 mm) allowance for mastic and tile.

TRANSFER SHOWER
  Rough-in Considerations

A bathroom plan should detail:
- Transfer shower width and depth.
- Drain location.
- Net thickness of each structural wall and wall covering.
- Grab bar, spray bar, and seat backing locations.
- Control valve location.
- Clear floor space.
- Recessed floor, built-up floor, and shower floor assembly detailing drainage and an accessible transition to the bathroom floor.
- All finished floor heights.
- Turning space to and away from a transfer shower.

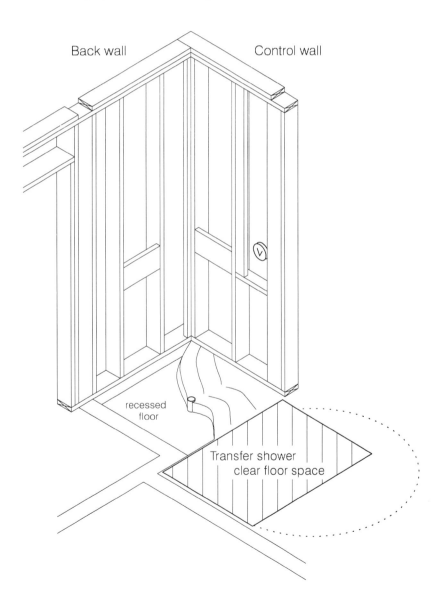

Back wall

Control wall

recessed
floor

Transfer shower
clear floor space

ALTERNATE SHOWER WITH SEAT (end wall controls)
Design Considerations

An alternate shower has a minimum width and, like the transfer shower, has 36 inches (914 mm) between the seat wall and the wall opposite it. Also, an alternate shower with seat's controls and shower spray unit are installed either on the end wall adjacent to the seat or on the back wall opposite the seat.

This shower's advantage is it allows a person to roll in and, with the aid of the back wall grab bar, transfer to a bathing seat.

A view of an alternate shower with seat, turning space, and fixture:
- Lavatory and alternate shower, page 140.

ALTERNATE SHOWER WITH SEAT'S
ADA COMPLIANT FIXTURES

SHOWER ENTRY
    36 inch (914 mm) wide

ALTERNATE SHOWER
1 - 60 inch by 36 inch
    (1524 x 914 mm)
    Alternate shower

1 - Rectangular
    folding seat

1 - Shower controls

1 - Shower spray unit

1 - 12 inch (305 mm)
    End wall grab bar

1 - 48 inch (1219 mm)
    Back wall grab bar

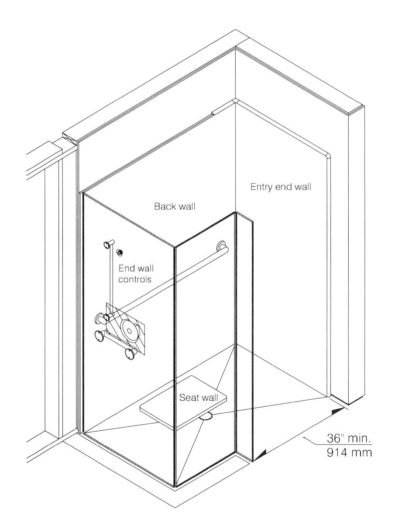

Entry end wall

Back wall

End wall
controls

Seat wall

36" min.
914 mm

Note: An L - shaped folding seat must have a clear path as it folds up past an adjacent grab bar. Coordinating the grab bar's height and length with a folding seat's height ensures a clear path to the seat wall. An example is on page 198.

ALTERNATE SHOWER WITH SEAT (end wall controls)
Typical Guidelines

ENTRY and SEAT WALL

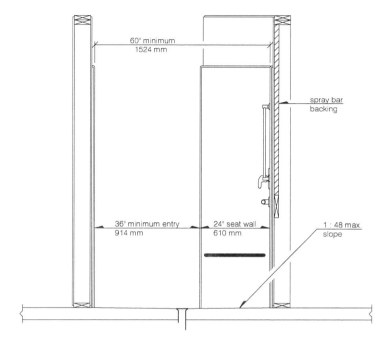

ALTERNATE SHOWER ENTRY
36 inches (914 mm) minimum
in width.

ALTERNATE SHOWER WIDTH
60 inches (1524 mm) minimum
from the entry end wall to the
end wall opposite it.

- A 72 inch (1829 mm) wide shower
  provides the space for a 36 inch
  (914 mm) wide seat wall.

ALTERNATE SHOWER DEPTH
36 inches (914 mm) from the seat wall
to the back wall.

SHOWER FLOOR TO BATHROOM FLOOR
CHANGE IN LEVEL
a. One-quarter inch (6.35 mm) maximum
   vertical change in level.
b. One-half inch (12.7 mm) maximum
   beveled change in level.

SHOWER FLOOR SLOPE
1 : 48 maximum cross slope and
running slope.

END WALL
(end wall controls)

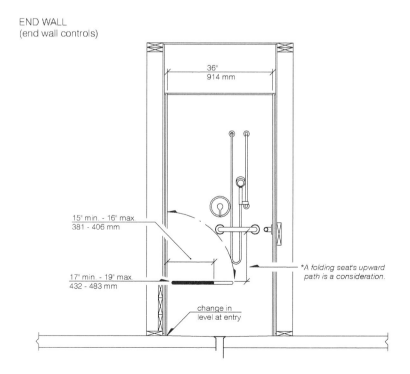

SEAT WIDTH
Must comply with the open side setback
and the adjacent side setback.

- Both setbacks are on page 208.

SEAT HEIGHT
17 inches (432 mm) minimum and
19 inches (483 mm) maximum
above the shower's finished floor.

*The space between a folding seat's
 L portion and the end wall grab bar
 is a consideration. An example is on
 page 198.

SEAT DEPTH
15 inches (381 mm) minimum and
16 inches (406 mm) maximum
from the seat wall.

ALTERNATE SHOWER WITH SEAT (end wall controls)
Typical Guidelines

END WALL
(end wall controls)

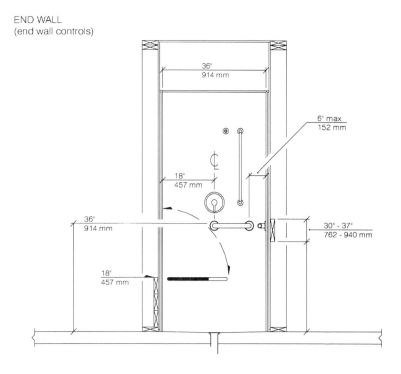

GRAB BAR HEIGHT (typical)
   a. Installed a uniform horizontal height
       above the finished floor.
   b. 33 inches (838 mm) minimum and
       36 inches (914 mm) maximum
       from the top of the gripping surface
       to the shower's finished floor.

Note the end wall grab bar's height and
length considerations below.

END WALL GRAB BAR
   a. Grab bars are not installed above
       the seat.
   b. Height and Length - An L - shaped
       folding seat must have a clear path
       as it folds up past an adjacent grab
       bar. Coordinating the grab bar's height
       and length with a folding seat's height
       ensures a clear path to the seat wall.
   c. 6 inches (152 mm) maximum
       from the back wall.

     ■ A 12 inch (305 mm) grab bar
       is illustrated.

BACK WALL GRAB BAR
   a. The same height as the end wall
       grab bar.
   b. The shower's width determines
       the grab bar's length.
   c. 6 inches (152 mm) maximum
       from the end wall.
   d. 6 inches (152 mm) maximum
       from the entry end wall.

     ■ A 48 inch (1219 mm) grab bar is
       illustrated.

BACK WALL

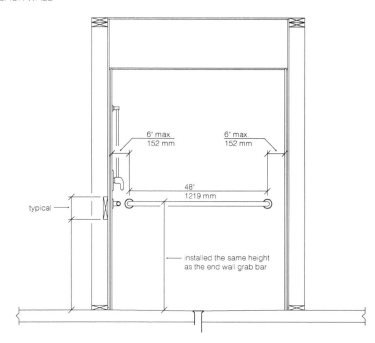

GRAB BAR BACKING (typical)
   30 inches to 37 inches (762 - 940 mm)
   above the finished floor.

SEAT BACKING
   Solid blocking from the finished floor to a
   point near the top of the seat.

     ■ 18 inches (457 mm) above the
       finished floor is illustrated.

ALTERNATE SHOWER WITH SEAT (end wall controls)
Typical Guidelines

An alternate shower with a
36 inch (914 mm) wide seat wall
and an L - shaped folding seat

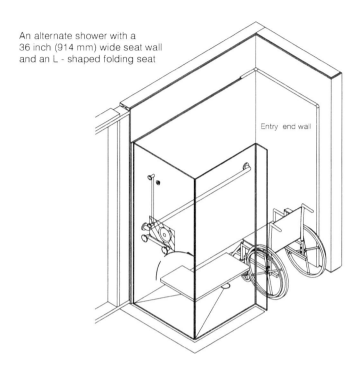

Entry end wall

CONTROL WALL
(end wall controls)

27" max
686 mm

*12"
305 mm

48" max
1219 mm

1-1/2" min
38.1 mm

1-1/2" min
38.1 mm

ALTERNATE SHOWER WITH SEAT
CONTROL WALL

An alternate shower with seat's controls
and shower spray unit are installed on
the end wall adjacent to the seat or on
the back wall opposite the seat.

The back wall controls and shower spray
unit are illustrated on page 205.

CONTROLS AND SHOWER SPRAY UNIT
END WALL LOCATION

Seat Wall Setback
27 inches (686 mm) maximum
from the seat wall.

*Seat Wall Setback Consideration
As an L - shaped seat folds up,
the L portion must have a clear
path past the grab bar, controls,
and a shower spray unit. Reach
is also a consideration.

Maximum Height
48 inches (1219 mm) maximum
above the shower's finished floor.

Minimum Height
1-1/2 inches (38.1 mm) minimum
above the end wall grab bar.

SHOWER SPRAY UNIT

Supply Hose
59 inches (1499 mm) minimum
in length.

Showerhead
Can be used both as a fixed showerhead
and as a handheld showerhead.

ALTERNATE SHOWER WITH SEAT (end wall controls)
Fixture Location

The location of a nearby fixture - in relation to an alternate
shower's entry - is an important consideration.

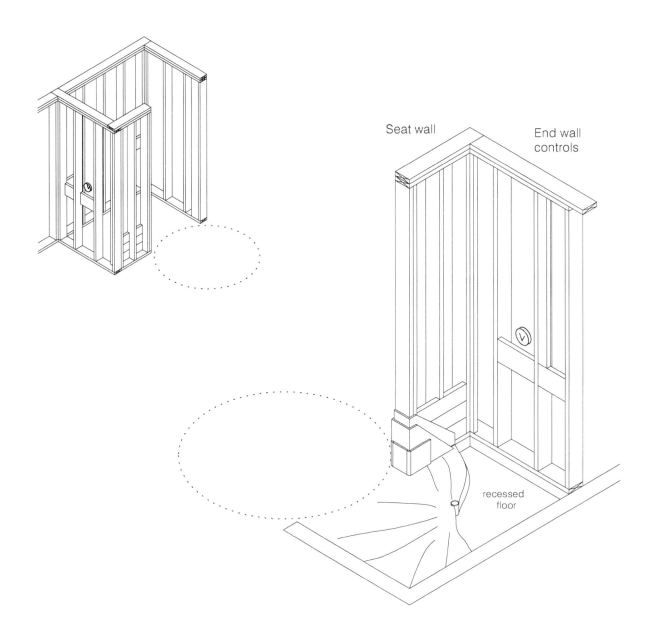

Seat wall

End wall
controls

recessed
floor

A typical shower surround has three plies.
    1st ply: 1/2 inch (12.7 mm) of water resistant wall board.
    2nd ply: 1/2 inch (12.7 mm) of cement board.
    3rd ply: 1/2 inch (12.7 mm) allowance for mastic and tile.

ALTERNATE SHOWER WITH SEAT (end wall controls)
Rough-in Considerations

A bathroom plan should detail:
- Alternate shower width, depth, unobstructed entry, and drain location.
- Net thickness of each structural wall and wall covering.
- Grab bar, spray bar, and seat backing locations.
- Control valve location.
- Recessed floor, built-up floor, and shower floor assembly detailing drainage and an accessible transition to the bathroom floor.
- All finished floor heights.
- Turning space to and away from an alternate shower.

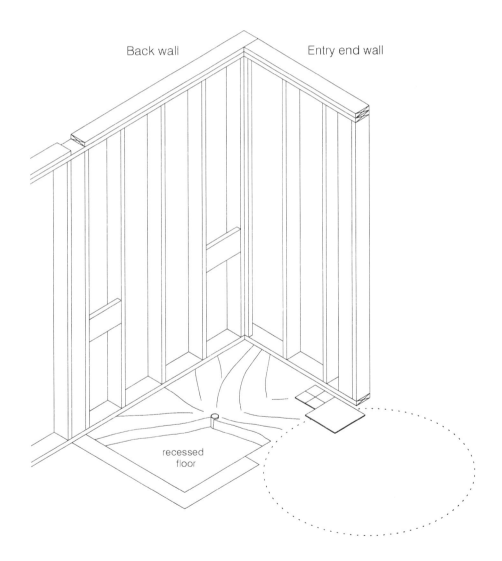

Back wall   Entry end wall

recessed
floor

ALTERNATE SHOWER WITH SEAT (back wall controls)
Design Considerations

Combining some of the design characteristics of a transfer
shower and an alternate shower creates a bathing fixture with
advantages.

- There is a grab bar forward of the approach to aid the
  transfer from wheelchair to seat.
- The seat wall is wide enough for an L - shaped folding seat.
- The folding seat, in an up position, gives the shower dual use.
- The shower spray unit and controls are opposite the seat.
- The showerhead, it its fixed position and when it is handheld,
  can have its spray directed away from the entrance.

A view of an alternate shower with seat, turning space, and a
cabinet and countertop is on page 156.

ALTERNATE SHOWER WITH SEAT'S
ADA COMPLIANT FIXTURES

SHOWER ENTRY
  36 inch (914 mm) wide

ALTERNATE SHOWER
1 - 72 inch by 36 inch
    (1829 x 914 mm)
    Alternate shower

1 - Transfer shower size
    L - shaped folding seat

1 - 12 inch (305 mm)
    End wall grab bar

1 - 60 inch (1524 mm)
    Back wall grab bar

1 - Shower controls

1 - Shower spray unit

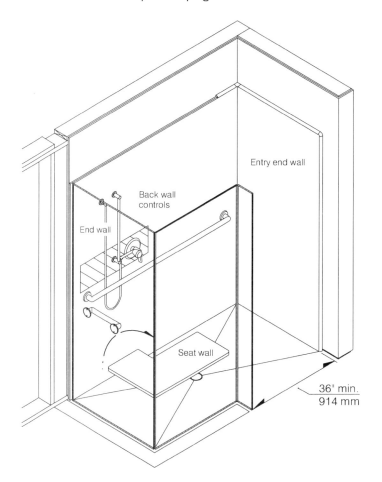

Note: An L - shaped folding seat must have a clear path as it
folds up past an adjacent grab bar. Coordinating the grab bar's
height and length with a folding seat's height ensures a clear path
to the seat wall. An example is on page 204.

ALTERNATE SHOWER WITH SEAT (back wall controls)
Typical Guidelines

ENTRY and SEAT WALL

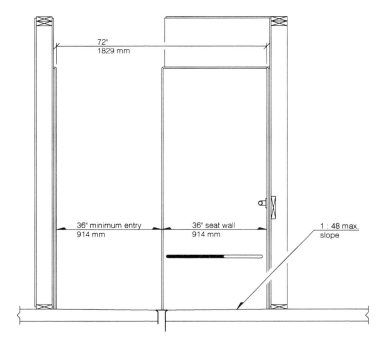

ALTERNATE SHOWER ENTRY
36 inches (914 mm) minimum
in width.

ALTERNATE SHOWER WIDTH
60 inches (1524 mm) minimum
from the entry end wall to the
end wall opposite it.

■ A 72 inch (1829 mm) wide shower
provides the space for a 36 inch
(914 mm) wide seat wall, a seat wall
wide enough to accommodate a
transfer shower size L - shaped seat.

ALTERNATE SHOWER DEPTH
36 inches (914 mm) from the seat wall
to the back wall.

SHOWER FLOOR TO BATHROOM FLOOR
CHANGE IN LEVEL
a. One-quarter inch (6.35 mm) maximum
vertical change in level.
b. One-half inch (12.7 mm) maximum
beveled change in level.

SHOWER FLOOR SLOPE
1 : 48 maximum cross slope and
running slope.

END WALL

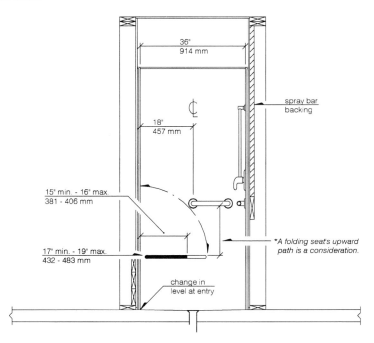

SEAT WIDTH
Must comply with the open side setback
and the adjacent side setback.

■ Both setbacks are on page 208.

SEAT HEIGHT
17 inches (432 mm) minimum and
19 inches (483 mm) maximum
above the shower's finished floor.

*The space between a folding seat's
L portion and the end wall grab bar
is a consideration. An example is on
page 204.

SEAT DEPTH
15 inches (381 mm) minimum and
16 inches (406 mm) maximum
from the seat wall.

ALTERNATE SHOWER WITH SEAT (back wall controls)
Typical Guidelines

END WALL

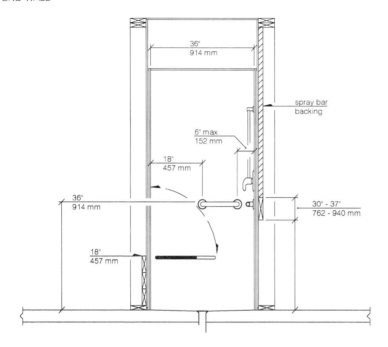

GRAB BAR HEIGHT (typical)
  a. Installed a uniform horizontal height
       above the finished floor.
  b. 33 inches (838 mm) minimum and
       36 inches (914 mm) maximum
       from the top of the gripping surface
       to the shower's finished floor.

*Note the end wall grab bar's height and
length considerations below.*

END WALL GRAB BAR
  a. Grab bars are not installed above
       the seat.
  b. Height and Length - An L - shaped
       folding seat must have a clear path
       as it folds up past an adjacent grab
       bar. Coordinating the grab bar's height
       and length with a folding seat's height
       ensures a clear path to the seat wall.
  c. 6 inches (152 mm) maximum
       from the back wall.

       ■ A 12 inch (305 mm) grab bar
          is illustrated.

BACK WALL
(back wall controls)

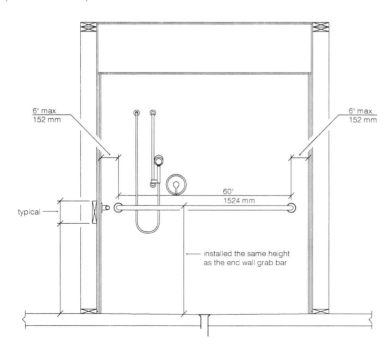

BACK WALL GRAB BAR
  a. The same height as the end wall
       grab bar.
  b. The shower's width determines
       the grab bar's length.
  c. 6 inches (152 mm) maximum
       from the end wall.
  d. 6 inches (152 mm) maximum
       from the entry end wall.

       ■ A 60 inch (1524 mm) grab bar is
          illustrated.

GRAB BAR BACKING (typical)
  30 inches to 37 inches (762 - 940 mm)
  above the finished floor.

SEAT BACKING
  Solid blocking from the finished floor to a
  point near the top of the seat.

       ■ 18 inches (457 mm) above the
          finished floor is illustrated.

ALTERNATE SHOWER WITH SEAT (back wall controls)
Typical Guidelines

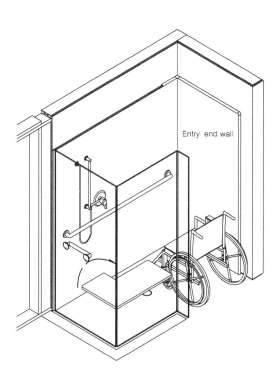

Entry end wall

CONTROL WALL
(back wall controls)

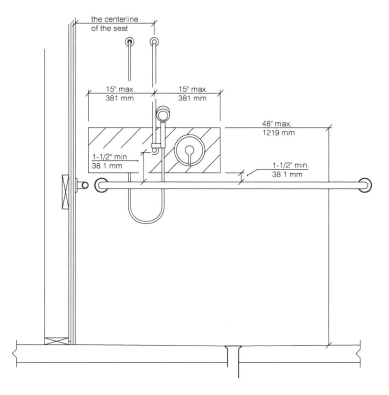

the centerline
of the seat

15" max.
381 mm

15" max.
381 mm

48" max.
1219 mm

1-1/2" min.
38.1 mm

1-1/2" min.
38.1 mm

ALTERNATE SHOWER WITH SEAT
CONTROL WALL

An alternate shower with seat's controls
and shower spray unit are installed on
the end wall adjacent to the seat or on
the back wall opposite the seat.

The end wall controls and shower spray
unit are illustrated on page 199.

SHOWER SPRAY UNIT AND CONTROLS
BACK WALL LOCATION

Centerline and Setback
The centerline of the seat to
15 inches (381 mm) maximum
on either side of the centerline
of the seat.

Maximum Height
48 inches (1219 mm) maximum
above the shower's finished floor.

Minimum Height
1-1/2 inches (38.1 mm) minimum
above the back wall grab bar.

SHOWER SPRAY UNIT

Supply Hose
59 inches (1499 mm) minimum
in length.

Showerhead
Can be used both as a fixed showerhead
and as a handheld showerhead.

ALTERNATE SHOWER WITH SEAT (back wall controls)
Fixture Location

The location of a nearby fixture - in relation to an alternate
shower's entrance - is an important consideration.

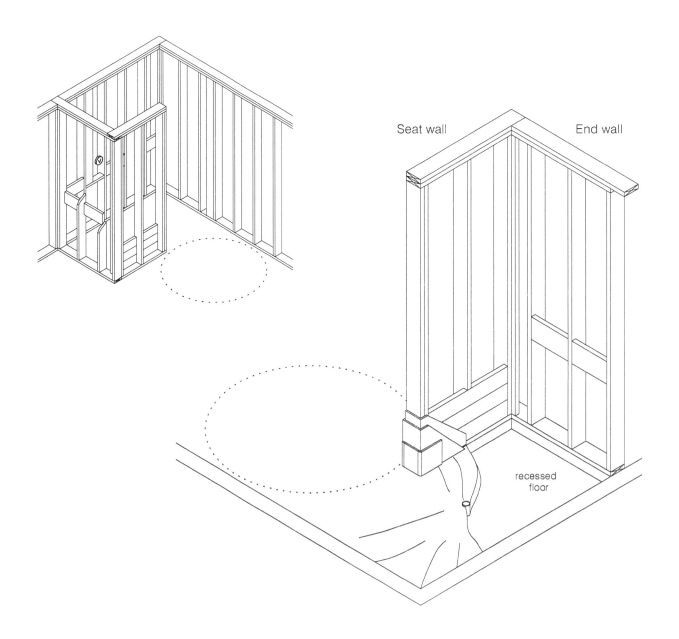

Seat wall   End wall

recessed
floor

A typical shower surround has three plies.
   1st ply: 1/2 inch (12.7 mm) of water resistant wall board.
   2nd ply: 1/2 inch (12.7 mm) of cement board.
   3rd ply: 1/2 inch (12.7 mm) allowance for mastic and tile.

ALTERNATE SHOWER WITH SEAT (back wall controls)
Rough-in Considerations

A bathroom plan should detail:
- Alternate shower width, depth, unobstructed entry, and drain location.
- Net thickness of each structural wall and wall covering.
- Grab bar, spray bar, and seat backing locations.
- Control valve location.
- Recessed floor, built-up floor, and shower floor assembly detailing drainage and an accessible transition to the bathroom floor.
- All finished floor heights.
- Turning space to and away from an alternate shower.

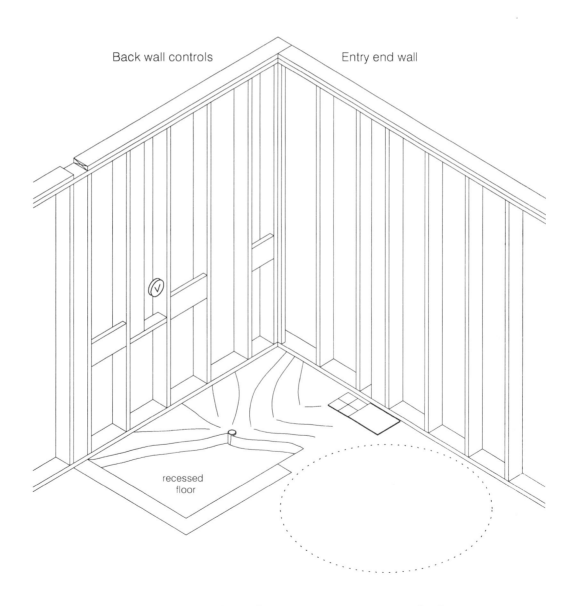

Back wall controls

Entry end wall

recessed
floor

SEAT WALL
Entry Side and Adjacent Side Setbacks

SEAT WALL

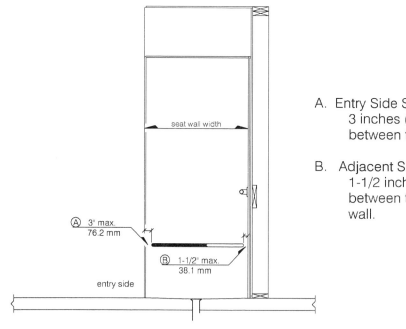

A. Entry Side Setback
3 inches (76.2 mm) maximum
between the entry and the seat.

B. Adjacent Side Setback
1-1/2 inches (38.1 mm) maximum
between the seat and the adjacent
wall.

ADJACENT WALL

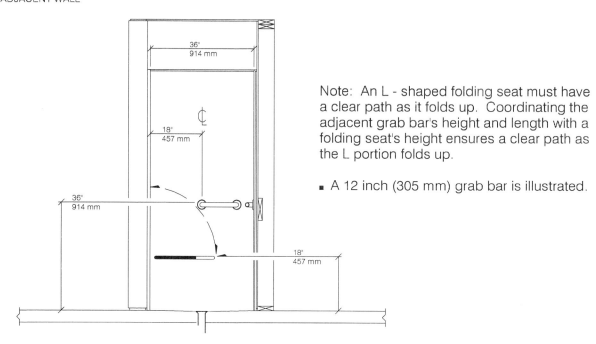

Note: An L - shaped folding seat must have
a clear path as it folds up. Coordinating the
adjacent grab bar's height and length with a
folding seat's height ensures a clear path as
the L portion folds up.

■ A 12 inch (305 mm) grab bar is illustrated.

ADA COMPLIANT BATHING SEAT
Planning and Availability

Planning is required at all shower compartments.

- What is the seat wall's width?
- Is an ADA complaint seat available for that seat wall width?
- How many working days are between order and delivery?
- Does a transfer shower size L - shaped folding seat best fit planning and availability?
- What are the heights of the shower's finished floor, the seat, and the grab bar adjacent to the seat?
- Does the seat have a clear path as it folds up?

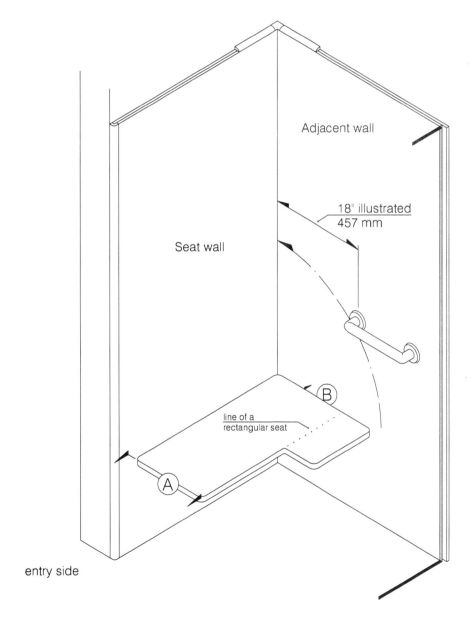

Adjacent wall

18" illustrated
457 mm

Seat wall

B

line of a
rectangular seat

A

entry side

NOTES

KITCHEN

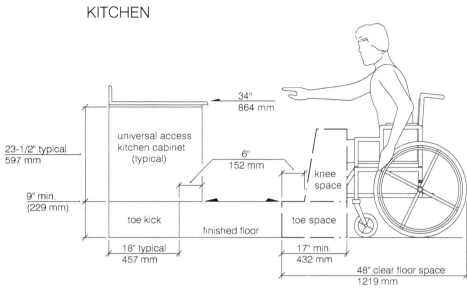

universal access
kitchen cabinet
(typical)

34"
864 mm

23-1/2" typical
597 mm

6"
152 mm

knee
space

9" min.
(229 mm)

toe kick

finished floor

toe space

18" typical
457 mm

17" min.
432 mm

48" clear floor space
1219 mm

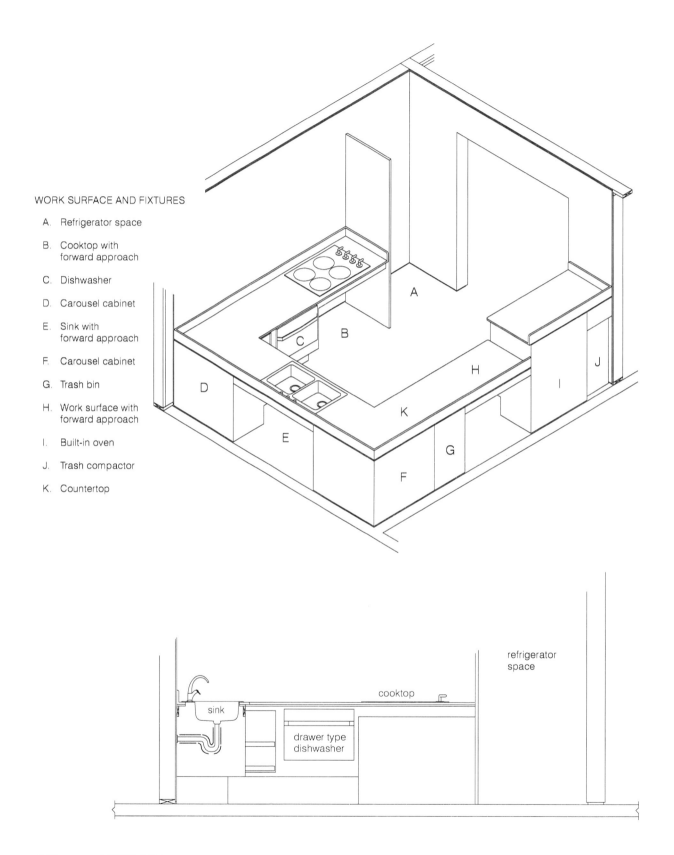

WORK SURFACE AND FIXTURES

A. Refrigerator space

B. Cooktop with
   forward approach

C. Dishwasher

D. Carousel cabinet

E. Sink with
   forward approach

F. Carousel cabinet

G. Trash bin

H. Work surface with
   forward approach

I. Built-in oven

J. Trash compactor

K. Countertop

refrigerator
space

cooktop

sink

drawer type
dishwasher

KITCHEN
Design Considerations

Wheelchair accessibility asks that every path, every space,
and every fixture receive special consideration. In a kitchen,
that special consideration begins with the countertop's height.

- Height of an obstruction at a parallel approach: 34 inches (864 mm)
  maximum above the finished floor, pages 82 and 83.

- Height of a kitchen work surface: 34 inches maximum
  above the finished floor, page 216.

- Height of a kitchen sink: 34 inches maximum
  above the finished floor, page 216.

Keeping the majority of the kitchen countertops a consistent height
quickly becomes a consideration. In the kitchen section, except
over an elevated cabinet, countertops are pictured at 33-3/4 inches
(857 mm) above the finished floor.

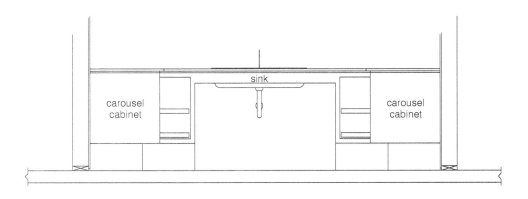

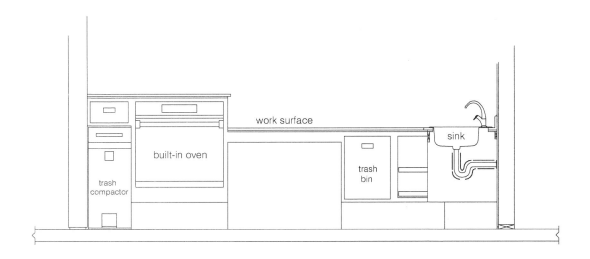

CABINET STRUCTURE
Toe Kick Height

A toe kick is installed. To create an accessible toe space, the top of the toe kick is, at minimum, 9 inches (229 mm) above the finished floor.

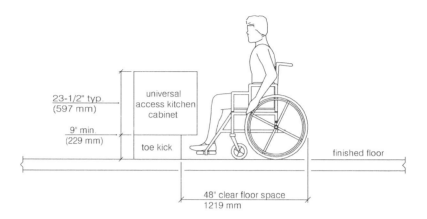

23-1/2" typ.
(597 mm)

universal access kitchen cabinet

9" min.
(229 mm)

toe kick

finished floor

48" clear floor space
1219 mm

Note: The thickness of any installed floor is an important consideration. Regardless of the application - bare concrete, tile, carpet, or any other application - the finished floor is the accessible floor surface a wheelchair travels on.

OPENINGS AND TOE KICKS

A. 37 inch (940 mm)
    Refrigerator space

B. 40 inch (1016 mm)
    Cooktop space

C. 27 inch (686 mm)
    Toe kick

D. 36 inch by 36 inch
    (914 x 914 mm)
    L - shaped toe kick

E. 48 inch (1219 mm)
    Sink space

F. 36 inch by 36 inch
    (914 x 914 mm)
    L - shaped toe kick

G. 18 inch (457 mm)
    Toe kick

H. 39 inch (991 mm)
    Work surface space

I. 33 inch (838 mm)
    Toe kick

J. 15 inch (381 mm)
    Trash compactor space

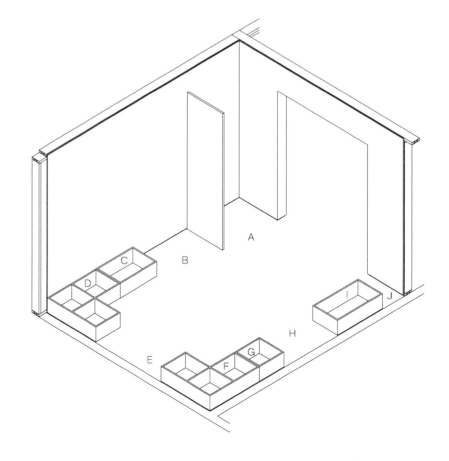

CABINET STRUCTURE
Cabinet and Countertop Height

A 23-1/2 inch (597 mm) tall universal access cabinet is installed above the toe kick.

This cabinet with a 1/2 inch (12.7 mm) plywood cap and a 3/4 inch (19.05 mm) thick countertop brings the top of the countertop to a height of 33-3/4 inches (857 mm) above the finished floor.

OPENINGS, TOE KICKS,
SUPPORTS, AND CABINETS

A. 37 inch (940 mm)
    Refrigerator space

B. 40 inch (1016 mm)
    Countertop support

C. 27 inch (686 mm)
    Drawer type
    dishwasher cabinet

D. 36 inch by 36 inch
    (914 x 914 mm)
    L - shaped
    carousel cabinet

E. 48 inch (1219 mm)
    Countertop support

F. 36 inch by 36 inch
    (914 x 914 mm)
    L - shaped
    carousel cabinet

G. 18 inch (457 mm)
    Trash bin cabinet

H. 39 inch (991 mm)
    Countertop support

I. 33 inch (838 mm)
    Elevated
    built-in oven cabinet

J. 15 inch (381 mm)
    Drawer with
    trash compactor
    space below

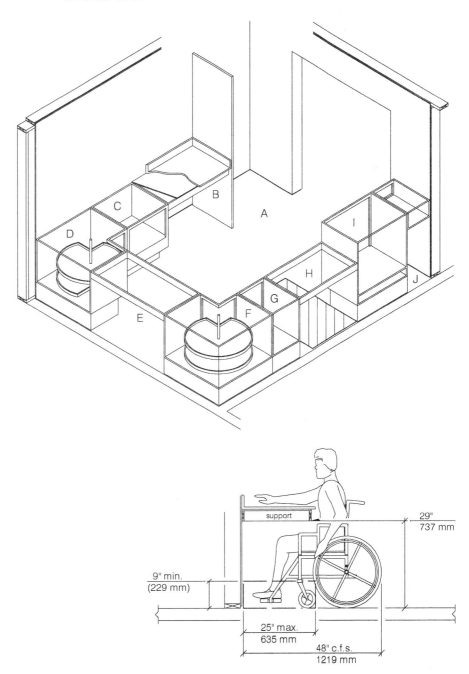

support

29"
737 mm

9" min.
(229 mm)

25" max.
635 mm

48" c.f.s.
1219 mm

CABINET STRUCTURE

Work Surface
   a. At minimum, one 30 inch (762 mm) wide section
      of countertop.
   b. 34 inches (864 mm) maximum above the finished floor.
   c. A forward approach clear floor space with knee and
      toe space.

Note: An oven with a bottom-hinged door has the work surface
adjacent to the door. An oven with a side-hinged door has the
work surface adjacent to the latch side of the door.

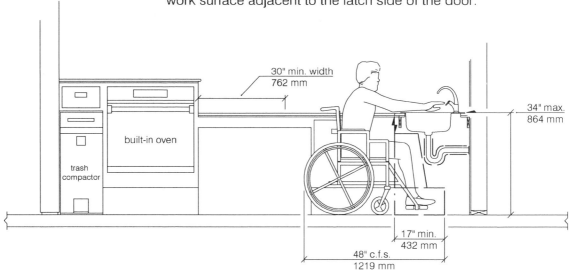

Sink
   a. 34 inches (864 mm) maximum above the finished floor.
   b. A forward approach clear floor space centered on the
      sink with knee and toe space.

Note: A typical kitchen sink's 1/4 inch (6.35 mm) lip and the
33-3/4 inch (857 mm) countertop height total 34 inches.

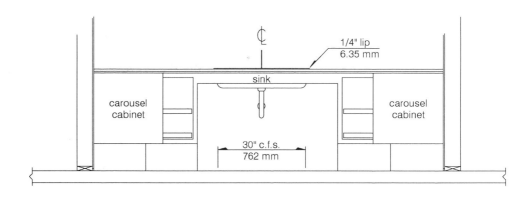

CABINET STRUCTURE
Fixtures

Clearance above, below, behind, and at both sides of a fixture are critical.

Typically, ADA compliant fixtures that require knee clearance have a specifications sheet that details:
- Knee and toe space.
- Fixture height above the finished floor.
- Fixture distance from the front of a countertop.
- Side wall, back wall, and cabinet structure's minimum clearance around heated elements, electrical hookups, gas hookups, drain assembly, supply lines, and the like.

OPENINGS AND FIXTURES

A. Refrigerator

B. Cooktop with forward approach

C. Dishwasher

D. Carousel cabinet

E. Sink with forward approach

F. Carousel cabinet

G. Trash bin

H. Work surface with forward approach

I. Built-in oven

J. Trash compactor

K. Countertop

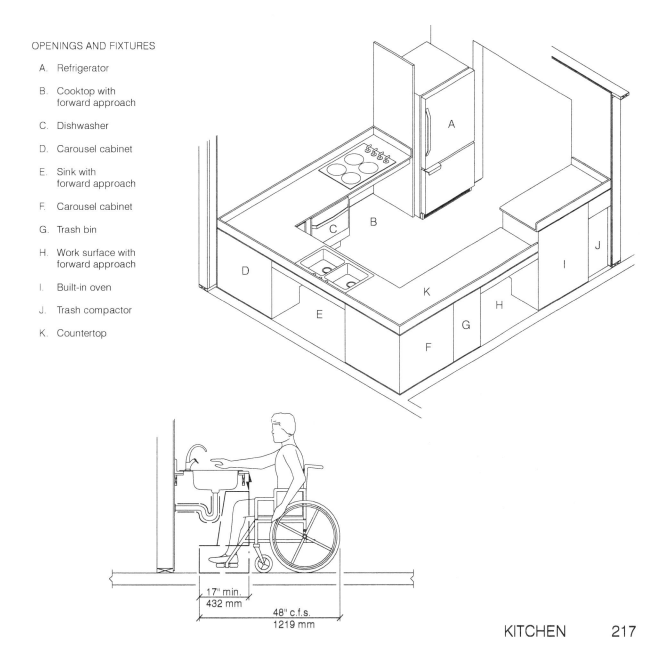

17" min.
432 mm

48" c.f.s.
1219 mm

APPROACH CLEAR FLOOR SPACE

- A kitchen fixture's forward or parallel approach clear floor space is centered on the fixture.
- A dishwasher's clear floor space is positioned adjacent to a dishwasher door. An example is on page 224.
- A work surface is positioned adjacent to an oven door. Guidelines and a note are on page 216.

Note: An open fixture door should have, at minimum, a 30 inch (762 mm) wide clearance in front of it.

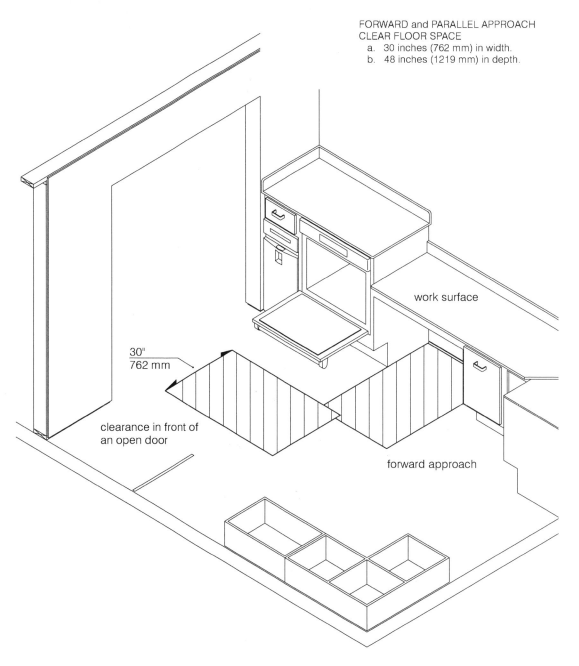

FORWARD and PARALLEL APPROACH
CLEAR FLOOR SPACE
   a. 30 inches (762 mm) in width.
   b. 48 inches (1219 mm) in depth.

work surface

30"
762 mm

clearance in front of
an open door

forward approach

HIGH AND LOW REACH

Typical high and low reach guidelines are:
- 44 inch (1118 mm) maximum obstructed high forward reach, page 78.
- 48 inch (1219 mm) maximum obstructed high parallel reach, page 83.
- 15 inch (381 mm) minimum unobstructed low parallel reach, page 81.

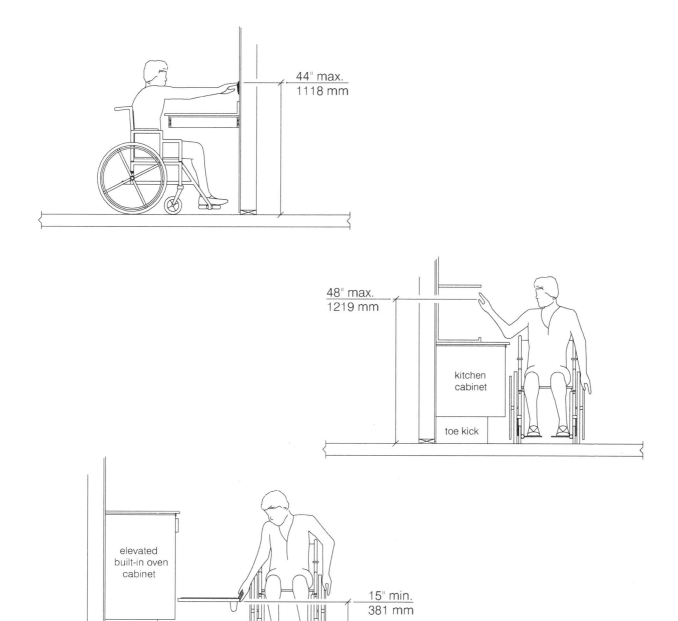

44" max.
1118 mm

48" max.
1219 mm

kitchen cabinet

toe kick

elevated built-in oven cabinet

toe kick

15" min.
381 mm

U - SHAPED KITCHEN
   a. U - shaped kitchens have three connected sides and
       one entrance.
   b. 90 degrees to the entrance, 60 inches (1524 mm) is the
       minimum distance between any combination of opposing
       countertops, cabinets, appliances, or walls.

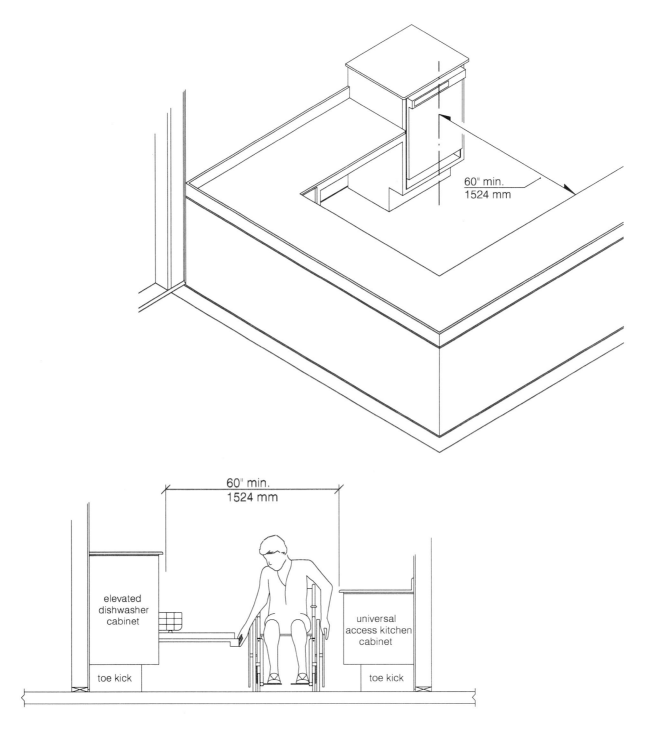

60" min.
1524 mm

60" min.
1524 mm

elevated
dishwasher
cabinet

universal
access kitchen
cabinet

toe kick

toe kick

PASS THROUGH KITCHEN

a. Pass through kitchens have two entrances in line with each other.

b. 40 inches (1016 mm) is the minimum distance between any combination of opposing countertops, cabinets, appliances, or walls.

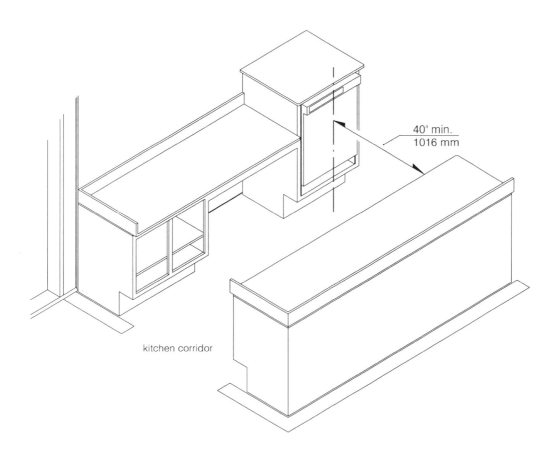

kitchen corridor

40" min.
1016 mm

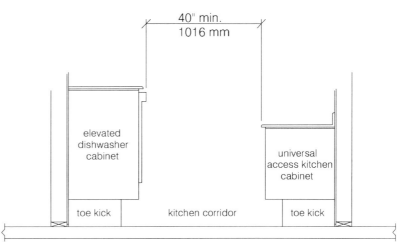

40" min.
1016 mm

elevated dishwasher cabinet

universal access kitchen cabinet

toe kick

kitchen corridor

toe kick

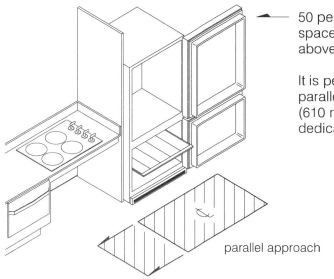

50 percent of a refrigerator-freezer's freezer space is 54 inches (1372 mm) maximum above the finished floor.

It is permitted to offset the refrigerator-freezer's parallel approach clear floor space 24 inches (610 mm) maximum from the centerline of the dedicated space.

FORWARD and PARALLEL APPROACH
CLEAR FLOOR SPACE
   a. 30 inches (762 mm) in width.
   b. 48 inches (1219 mm) in depth.

parallel approach

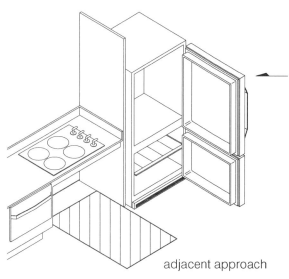

An adjacent approach has advantages.

An adjacent approach to a refrigerator-freezer allows a hand-to-hand transfer, from a shelf or pullout shelf, to a countertop.

adjacent approach

In this example, a forward approach to a cooktop is adjacent to a nearby fixture.

A parallel approach has space on both sides of a 30 inch (762 mm) wide cooktop.

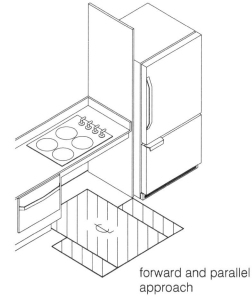

forward and parallel approach

APPROACH EXAMPLES
Refrigerator-Freezer and Cooktop

Clearance above, below, behind, and at both sides of a fixture are critical.

Typically, ADA compliant fixtures that require knee clearance have a specifications sheet that details:
- Knee and toe space.
- Fixture height above the finished floor.
- Fixture distance from the front of a countertop.
- Side wall, back wall, and cabinet structure's minimum clearance around heated elements, electrical hookups, gas hookups, drain assembly, supply lines, and the like.

Note: 36 inch (914 mm) wide paths from fixture to fixture and a circular turning space are illustrated below.

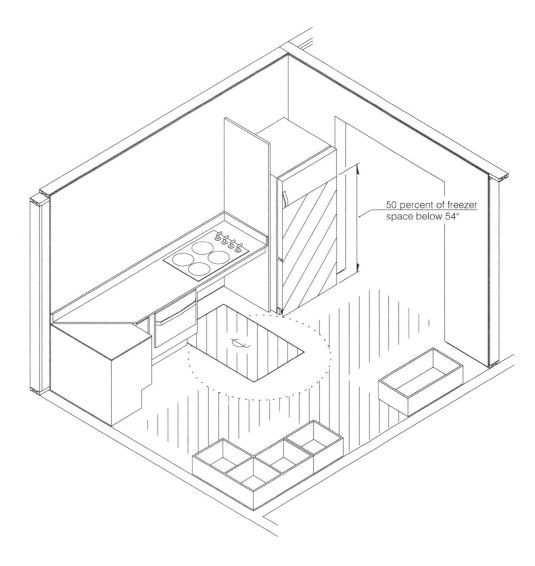

50 percent of freezer space below 54"

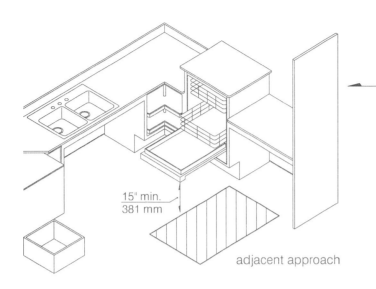

A dishwasher's clear floor space is positioned adjacent to a dishwasher door.

FORWARD and PARALLEL APPROACH
CLEAR FLOOR SPACE
a. 30 inches (762 mm) in width.
b. 48 inches (1219 mm) in depth.

15" min.
381 mm

adjacent approach

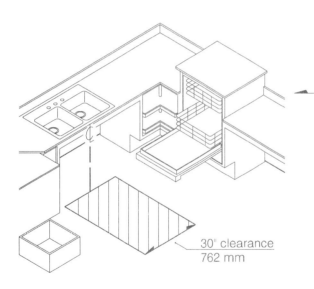

An open dishwasher door cannot obstruct a sink's or the dishwasher's clear floor space.

Note that the clearance in front of the open door is in line with the sink's centerline and forward approach clear floor space.

30" clearance
762 mm

A drawer type dishwasher has the advantage of keeping the countertop a uniform height. Again, the sink's clear floor space is beyond the open dishwasher door.

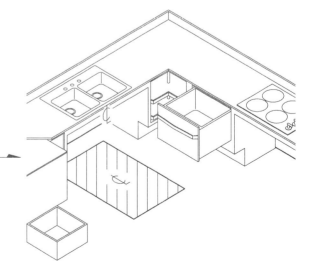

Making sure a person can enter a kitchen, use any fixture in any order, turn around and leave requires planning. It also requires answers to basic questions.

- Is a fixture readily available?

- Is there an accessible toe space below a cabinet?

- Which approach clear floor space makes a fixture accessible?

- Does a fixture require knee clearance?

- Where are a fixture's hard edges when its door is open? When closed?

- How does a turning space lead from one fixture to the remaining fixtures in the kitchen?

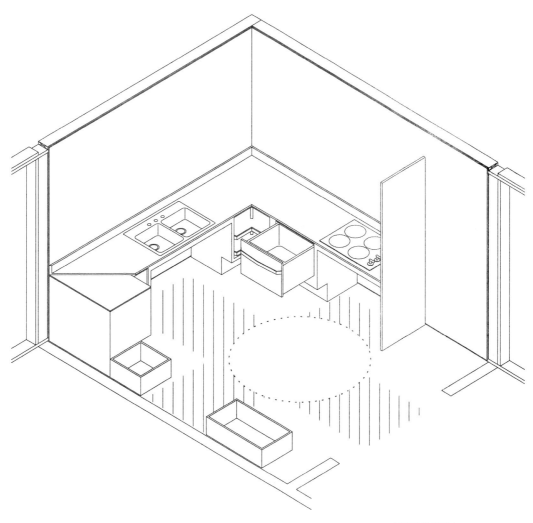

APPROACH EXAMPLES
Sink

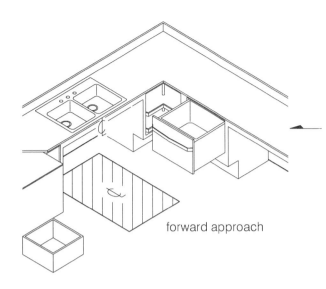

forward approach

The forward approach clear floor space, in concert with knee clearance, allows a person to keep both hands forward while the sink is being used.

FORWARD and PARALLEL APPROACH
CLEAR FLOOR SPACE
  a. 30 inches (762 mm) in width.
  b. 48 inches (1219 mm) in depth.

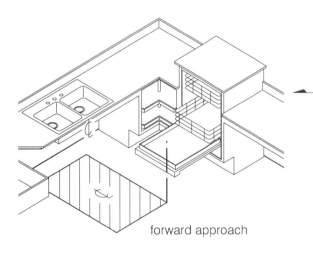

forward approach

Moving past the dishwasher's open door to the sink's forward approach clear floor space requires 30 inches (762 mm) of clearance beyond the open dishwasher door.

Again, the sink's clear floor space is beyond the open dishwasher door.

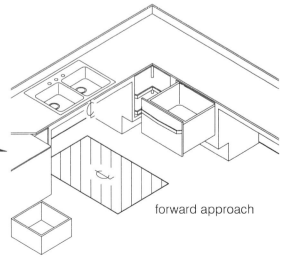

forward approach

APPROACH EXAMPLES
  Sink

Clearance above, below, behind, and at both sides of a fixture
are critical.

Typically, ADA compliant fixtures that require knee clearance
have a specifications sheet that details:
- Knee and toe space.
- Fixture height above the finished floor.
- Fixture distance from the front of a countertop.
- Side wall, back wall, and cabinet structure's minimum
  clearance around heated elements, electrical hookups,
  gas hookups, drain assembly, supply lines, and the like.

Note: 36 inch (914 mm) wide paths from fixture to fixture and a
circular turning space are illustrated below.

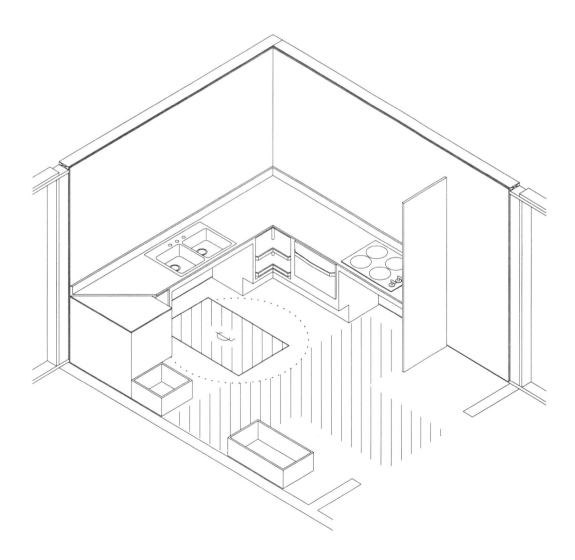

APPROACH EXAMPLES
Work Surface

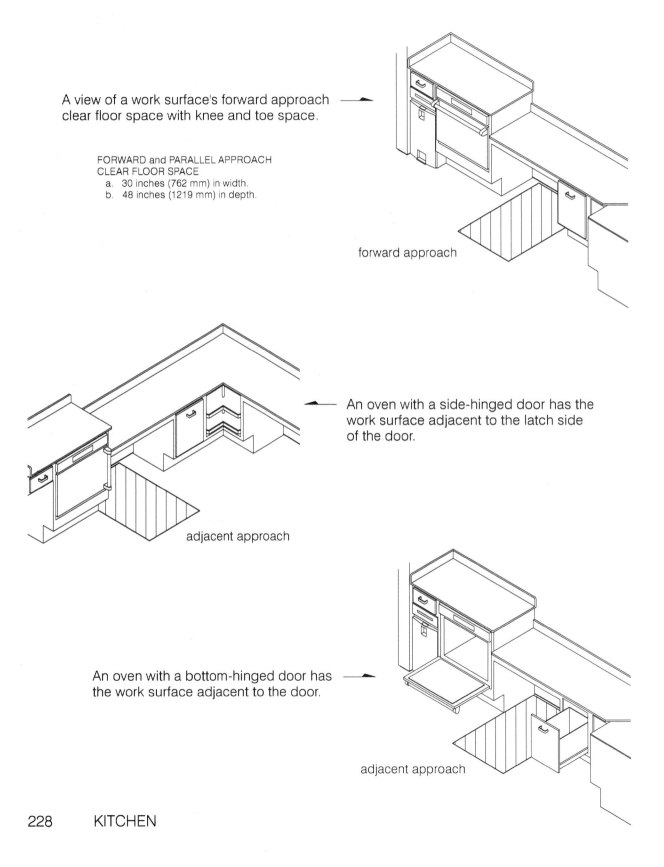

A view of a work surface's forward approach clear floor space with knee and toe space. ➡

FORWARD and PARALLEL APPROACH
CLEAR FLOOR SPACE
   a.   30 inches (762 mm) in width.
   b.   48 inches (1219 mm) in depth.

forward approach

⬅ An oven with a side-hinged door has the work surface adjacent to the latch side of the door.

adjacent approach

An oven with a bottom-hinged door has the work surface adjacent to the door. ➡

adjacent approach

Making sure a person can enter a kitchen, use any fixture in any order, turn around and leave requires planning. It also requires answers to basic questions.

- Is a fixture readily available?

- Is there an accessible toe space below a cabinet?

- Which approach clear floor space makes a fixture accessible?

- Does a fixture require knee clearance?

- Where are a fixture's hard edges when its door is open? When closed?

- How does a turning space lead from one fixture to the remaining fixtures in the kitchen?

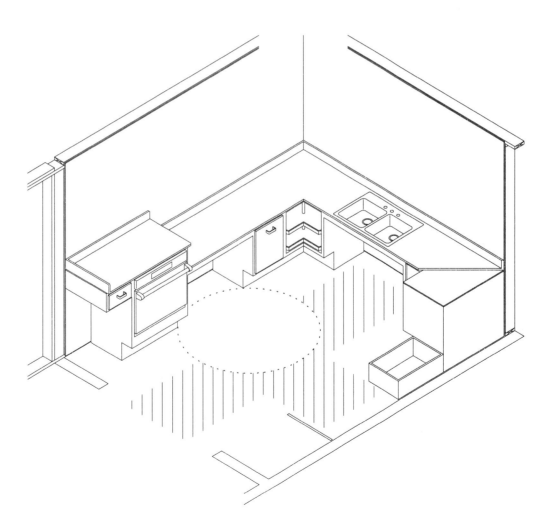

APPROACH EXAMPLES
Range

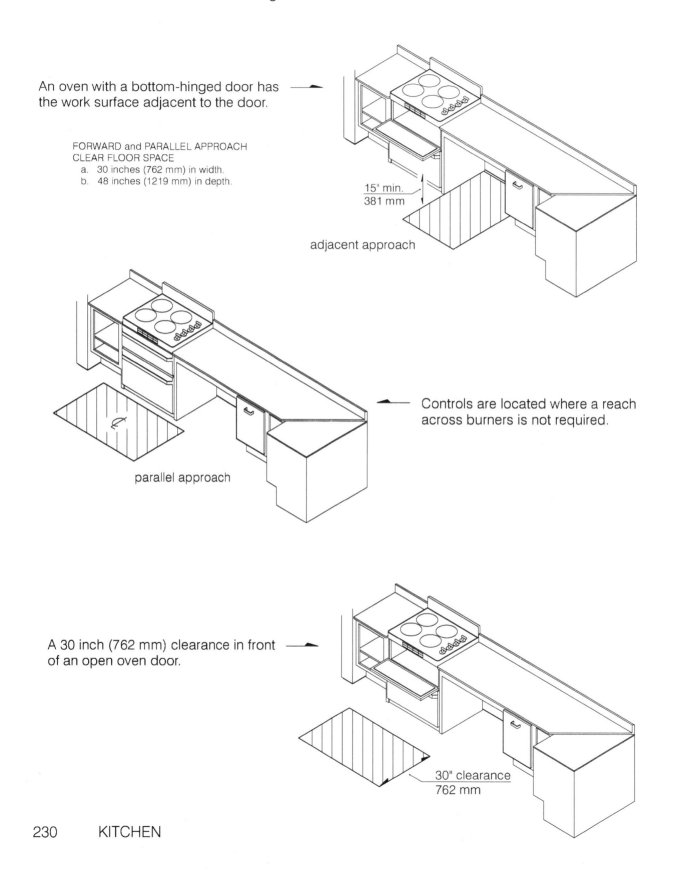

An oven with a bottom-hinged door has the work surface adjacent to the door. →

FORWARD and PARALLEL APPROACH
CLEAR FLOOR SPACE
   a. 30 inches (762 mm) in width.
   b. 48 inches (1219 mm) in depth.

15" min.
381 mm

adjacent approach

parallel approach

← Controls are located where a reach across burners is not required.

A 30 inch (762 mm) clearance in front of an open oven door. →

30" clearance
762 mm

Making sure a person can enter a kitchen, use any fixture in any order, turn around and leave requires planning. It also requires answers to basic questions.

- Is a fixture readily available?

- Is there an accessible toe space below a cabinet?

- Which approach clear floor space makes a fixture accessible?

- Does a fixture require knee clearance?

- Where are a fixture's hard edges when its door is open? When closed?

- How does a turning space lead from one fixture to the remaining fixtures in the kitchen?

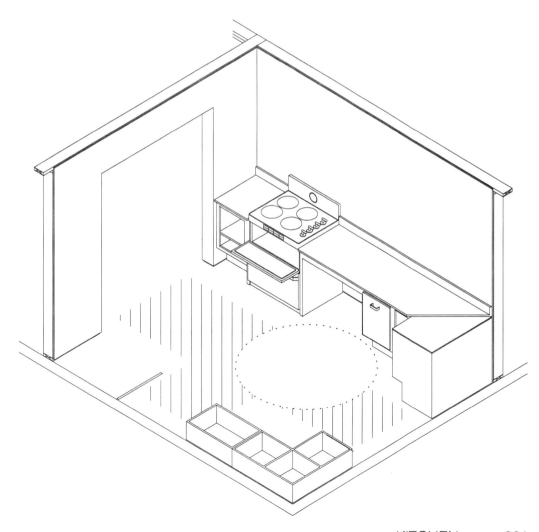

APPROACH EXAMPLES
Built-in Oven

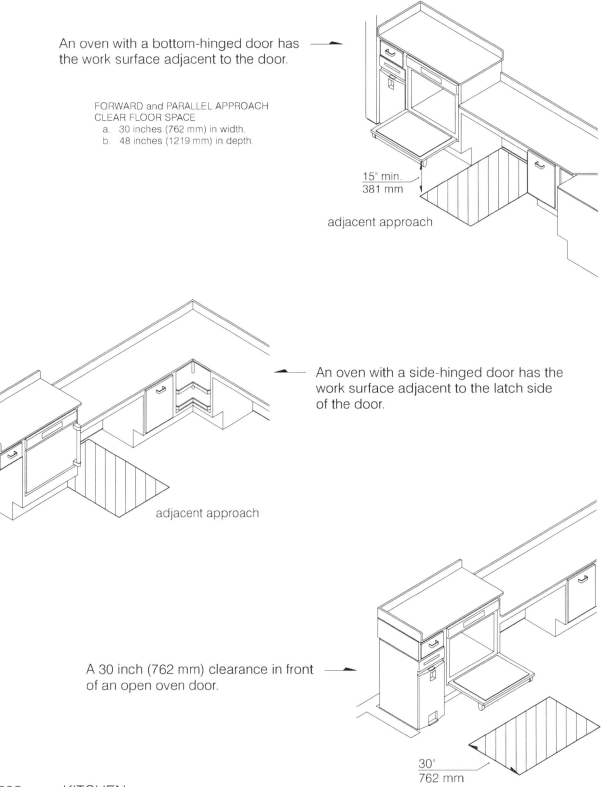

An oven with a bottom-hinged door has the work surface adjacent to the door.

FORWARD and PARALLEL APPROACH
CLEAR FLOOR SPACE
   a.   30 inches (762 mm) in width.
   b.   48 inches (1219 mm) in depth.

15" min.
381 mm

adjacent approach

An oven with a side-hinged door has the work surface adjacent to the latch side of the door.

adjacent approach

A 30 inch (762 mm) clearance in front of an open oven door.

30"
762 mm

Making sure a person can enter a kitchen, use any fixture in any order, turn around and leave requires planning. It also requires answers to basic questions.

- Is a fixture readily available?

- Is there an accessible toe space below a cabinet?

- Which approach clear floor space makes a fixture accessible?

- Does a fixture require knee clearance?

- Where are a fixture's hard edges when its door is open? When closed?

- How does a turning space lead from one fixture to the remaining fixtures in the kitchen?

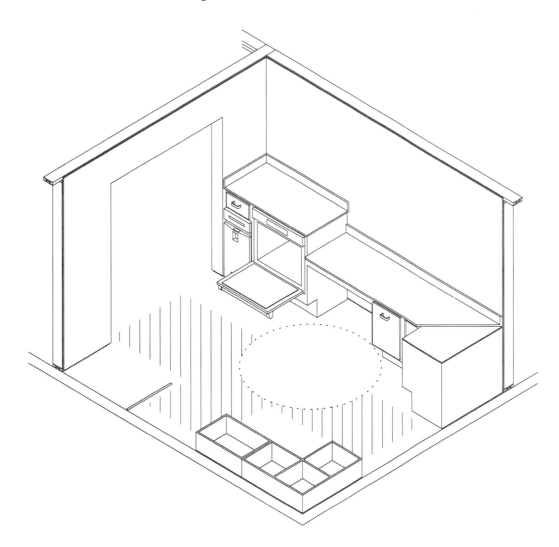

FIXTURE HEIGHT AND LOCATION

A taller cabinet, housing an elevated appliance, provides the height and location for an appliance that does not fit under a 33-3/4" (857 mm) tall kitchen countertop.

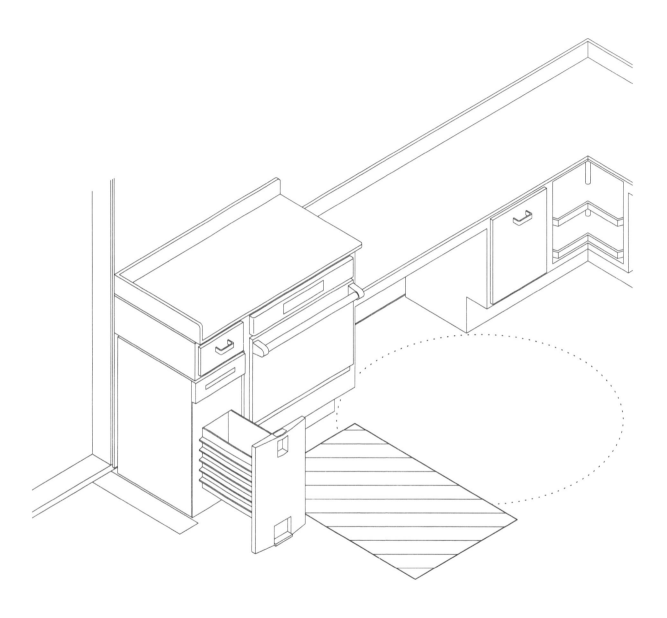

MANEUVERING INSIDE A KITCHEN

Below, circular turning spaces illustrate how approach space and turning space overlap, providing a path from one fixture to another.

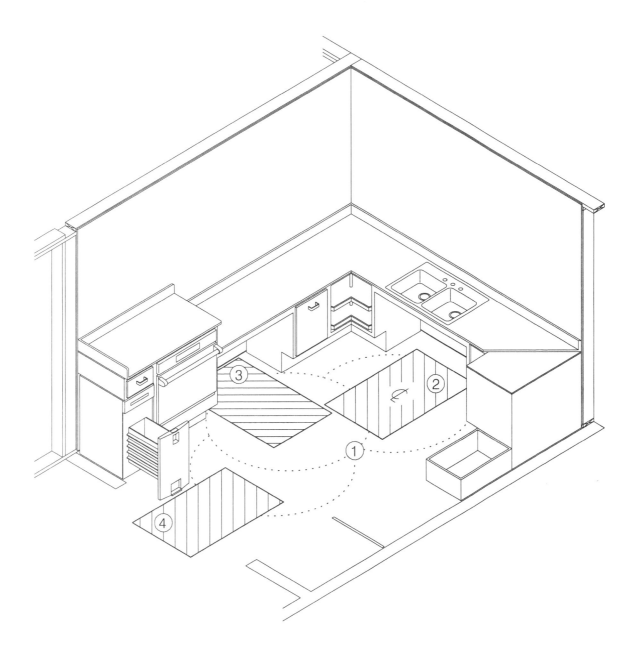

Overlapping Spaces
1. Circular turning spaces.
2. Sink forward approach clear floor space.
3. Work surface forward approach clear floor space.
4. Clearance in front of a trash compactor door.

ACKNOWLEDGMENTS

I am particularly indebted to my wife, Anna, for her
patience, critiques, and affection throughout a project
that often appeared endless.

I also thank Bob and Maria Braken, Sara Edelman,
Sanaa Hussain, Teresa Jennings, Star Lawrence,
Joseph Mellman, Maria Luisa Mellman, Jerry Simpson,
Kevin Taylor, William Wilson, and Elizabeth Yoo for all
of their help and for taking the time to send ADA related
articles.

Graphic designers Pia and Uwe Seifert sent examples
of European accessibility specifications and proposed
the relationship between pictures and text.

Dr. Alan Shulman, NYC, New York, also realized the need
for this guide and encouraged this project from the beginning.

Jacqueline Waters' insights and critical readings gave the
The Right Space a polish it would not otherwise have had.
I am indebted to her.

THE AUTHOR

Albert M. Ayala is a general contractor who designs and
builds homes in central Arizona. He began writing this
guide after his mother, at age 89, fractured her tibia and
came to live with him and his wife.